Five Anthems
for mixed voices & organ

Five Anthems for mixed voices & organ

Texts by Charles Wesley
Music by Malcolm Archer

Kevin
Mayhew

We hope you enjoy the music in this book. Further copies are available
from your local music shop or Christian bookshop.

In case of difficulty, please contact the publisher direct by writing to:

The Sales Department
KEVIN MAYHEW LTD
Rattlesden
Bury St Edmunds
Suffolk
IP30 0SZ

Phone 01449 737978
Fax 01449 737834

Please ask for our complete catalogue of outstanding Church Music.

First published in Great Britain in 1995 by Kevin Mayhew Ltd

ISBN 0 86209 639 1
Catalogue No: 1450033

Front Cover: Detail from a tapestry by William Morris (1834-1896).
Reproduced by courtesy of The William Morris Gallery, Walthamstow, London.
Photo: © Woodmansterne Picture Library.
Cover design by Juliette Clarke and Graham Johnstone.
Picture Research: Jane Rayson

Music Editor: Joanne Clarke
Music setting by Chris Hinkins

Printed and bound in Great Britain

Contents

Composer's Note

This suite of anthems was commissioned for the 1995 Charles Wesley Festival, and first performed in Bristol Cathedral on 17th June. The commission was funded by The Pratt Green Trust.

Although composed as a suite, the anthems are designed so that they can also be used separately for liturgical use.

Commissioned by The Pratt Green Trust
for the Charles Wesley Festival, Bristol Cathedral 1995

FIVE ANTHEMS
FOR MIXED VOICES AND ORGAN

Texts by Charles Wesley (1757-1834)
Music by Malcolm Archer (*b.*1952)

1. Christ, whose glory fills the skies

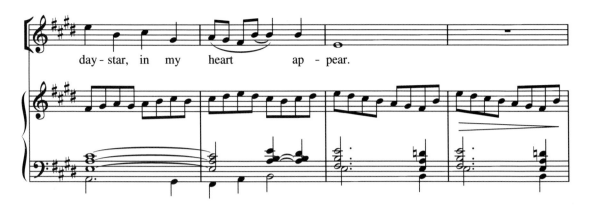

day-star, in my heart ap - pear.

S A: Dark and cheer-less is the morn un-ac-com-pa-nied by thee;

T B: Dark and cheer-less is the morn un-ac-com-pa-nied by thee;

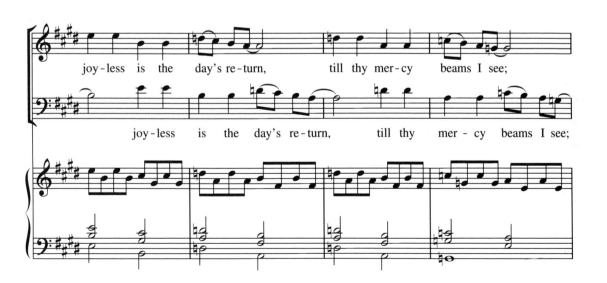

joy-less is the day's re-turn, till thy mer-cy beams I see;

joy-less is the day's re-turn, till thy mer-cy beams I see;

till thy in-ward light im-part, glad my eyes, and warm my

till thy in-ward light im-part, glad my eyes, and warm my

heart.

heart.

Vi - sit then this soul of mine,

pierce the gloom of sin and grief

fill me, ra - dian - cy di - vine,

scat-ter all my un-be-lief; more and more thy-self dis-play,

shin-ing to the per - fect day.

Christ, whose glo - ry

Christ, whose

day - star, in my heart ap - pear.

day - star, in my heart ap - pear.

high, be near; day - star, in my heart ap - pear.

A - men.

A - men.

T   A - men.
B

11

2. Thou God of truth and love

Flowing (♩ = 76)

Thou God of truth and love, we seek thy per-fect way, rea-dy thy choice to ap-prove, thy pro - vi-dence to o - bey: En - ter in-to thy

wise de-sign, and sweet-ly lose our will in thine.

Why hast thou cast our lot in this same age and

Ah,

place, and why to-ge-ther brought to see each o -

Ah,

we might one re-main? To-ge-ther tra-vel on, and

bear each o-ther's pain; till all thy ut-most good-ness prove

till all thy ut-most good-ness prove

relax tempo slightly

mf

prove and rise re-newed in per - fect

and rise re-newed in per-fect

3. Jesu, my truth, my way

4. Author of life divine

Adagio (♩ = 76)

Au - thor of life di - vine, who hast a ta - ble spread, fur - nished with my - stic wine and e - ver - last - ing bread, pre - serve the life thy - self hast giv'n, and feed and train us up for heaven.

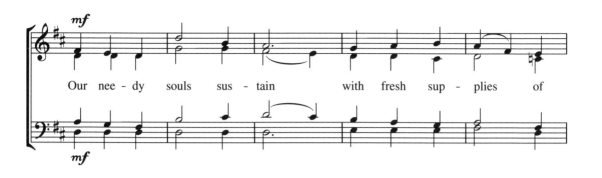

Our nee - dy souls sus - tain with fresh sup - plies of

love, till all thy life we gain, and all thy

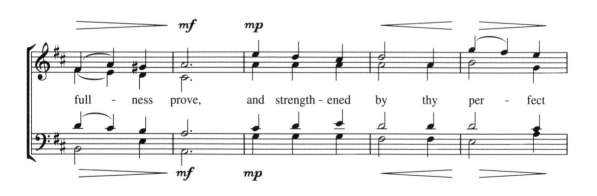

full - ness prove, and strength - ened by thy per - fect

grace, be - hold with - out a veil thy face.

5. Rejoice, the Lord is King

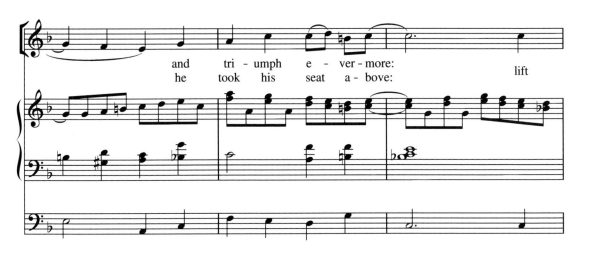

and tri - umph e - ver - more:
he took his seat a - bove: lift

up your hearts, lift up your voice, re - joice, a - gain I

say, re - joice.

His king - dom can - not fail;

can - not

he rules o'er earth and heaven;

he rules o'er earth and heaven; the

fail;

keys to death and hell are to our Je - sus given: lift

up your hearts, lift up your voice, re - joice, a - gain I say, re -

26

joice.

He

sits at God's right hand till all his foes sub-mit, and

bow to his com-mand and fall be - neath his feet:

lift up your hearts, lift up your voice, re -

joice, a - gain I say, re - joice.

Re - joice, the Lord is King,

Gt.

legato

your Lord and King a-dore; mor-tals, give thanks and sing,

and tri-umph e - ver-more: lift up your hearts, lift

up your voice, re - joice, a - gain I say, re -

staccato

joice.

Dartmouth
Ghosts & Mysteries

Tales of the town and its villages

dartmouth
ghosts & mysteries

tales of the town and its villages

ken taylor

Published in the United Kingdom in 2006 by Richard Webb

© Ken Taylor 2006

Photography by Valerie Wills, Dartmouth, Devon

Designed by Laurence Daeche, Anon Design Co., Christchurch, Dorset

A CIP catalogue record for this book is available from the British Library

ISBN 0-9536361-5-1
13 digit version
ISBN 978-0-9536361-5-0

Typesetting: Titling: Disturbance. Body copy: 9.5/12pt ITC Garamond

Printed and bound in the United Kingdom by Short Run Press, Exeter, Devon

RW.UK Ltd trading as Richard Webb, Publisher

Richard Webb, Publisher
Dartmouth, Devon, England

Dedication

We live surrounded by mysteries that hover like dreams on the fringe of consciousness, yet most of us avert our eyes, gazing chastely instead upon the bright icons in our sanctuary of science. Even here though, we may all sometimes glimpse wonders that lie beyond the veil of the merely mysterious, and some of us may do more — it is to these pioneers that this book is dedicated.

Disclaimer

These stories are offered in good faith, and the author has researched them as thoroughly as practical, and to the best of his knowledge they are all true in the sense that each witness has described an actual experience. However, the nature of anomalous phenomena makes it impossible to claim these stories are 'true' in the conventional sense of established fact (the English legal system, for example, disbelieves in ghosts). Therefore the interpretation of the experiences described is open to question, and no warranty can be given or should be inferred regarding the empirical existence of ghosts, UFOs, or other phenomena included here.

If you think you may have a problem with any aspect of the paranormal, seek suitably qualified help. But remember, supernatural events of whatever sort are rare — very rare — so don't have nightmares.

CREDITS

Original artwork and photography on the pages indicated is copyright:
Iris Pritchard 19; Jan Polinski 60, 61 & 62; Joules Taylor 92 & 93;
Ken Taylor 28, 77, 98, 99, 107, 108 & 111; Ursula Dimes 33.

The author has made every effort to find and correctly attribute the copyright
of material but if he has inadvertently used or accredited any material inappropriately,
please could the copyright holder contact him via the publisher so that full credit
can be given in the next edition.

Other books by Ken Taylor include:
*Prehistoric Hill Settlement Capton Tarot for Today The Early Heaven Oracle
Brislington Ghosts and Mysteries.*

And, in collaboration with his wife Joules:
Celtic Myths and Legends Clairvoyance Crystals.

For information about the author visit www.wavewrights.com,
and to share more true stories of the paranormal in the local area visit
www.smartgroups.com/groups/dartmouthghosts.

acknowledgements

Thanks to everyone mentioned in the text, and also to the following whose help and support, even if they had no tales to tell themselves, have significantly contributed to this project.

Debbie Abrahams, Jonathan Ansell, Tony Aylmer, Chips Barber, Andrew Barker, James Beer, Fae Blake, Gary Booker, Dudley Bucknell, Pat Catchpole, Anne-Marie Cattanach, Ralph Cawthorne, Darren Clarke, Gill Claydon, Marcea Colley, Richard Cranfield, Alix Crowther, Peter Crowther, Bill Dimes, Gloria Heather Dixon, Daniel Edwards, Brian Elliot, Chad Fine, Wally Fleet, Peter Franklin, Jessica Gardner, Carol Gertner, Rachel Gibson, Kate Gill, Theresa Head, Joss Hodges, Mary Hodges, Patricia Ingram, Sally Johnson, Helen Kerrison, Robin Kinloch, Bill Langford, Judy Lewthwaite, Joanne Logan, Karen Mander, Moira Mellor, Val Mercer, June Miles, Rosie Murdie, Celia Nash, Susi Nightingale, David Payne, Susan Pearson, Anthony Phillips, Hugh Pincott, Jason Plummer, Nic Ponticakis, John Ridalls, Renee Ruddlesden, Martin Ryan, Laurie Scott, Trystan Swale, Norman Symms, Joules Taylor, Kai Taylor, Gordon Thomas, Roy Thwaites, Brian Watson, Gilly Webb, Richard Webb, Z White, Susan Whiteway, Pam Wills.

contents

INTRODUCTION

ROUND EVERY CORNER IN DARTMOUTH LIES a DELIGHTFUL BLEND of HISTORY AND mystery WAITING TO BE DISCOVERED, AND ITS IMPORTANCE as a MARKET TOWN MEANS IT'S SURROUNDED BY a CRESCENT of ANCIENT HAMLETS AND VILLAGES — EACH WITH ITS OWN fascinating STORIES of THE SUPERNATURAL OR PARANORMAL. IT HAS BEEN a PLEASURE AND a PRIVILEGE to MEET AND CORRESPOND WITH SO MANY PEOPLE WHO HAVE ENTRUSTED THEIR STORIES TO ME.

This anthology preserves a wide range of local stories and, like a museum, protects people's experiences from being forgotten or changing so much in the re-telling that their kernel of truth is lost. I have taken pains to record these tales in a way that the witnesses are happy with — in effect I have been a ghost-writer for each and every one.

Sadly, the most frequent sort of ghost story cannot be found here, it is too intensely personal for people to share in public: the sudden awakening in the small hours to find your recently deceased loved-one watching over you. A psychologist might argue that such an experience is just part of the subconscious process of coming to terms with the loss of a cherished friend or relation: simply our yearnings manifesting as a powerful dream while we are in a hypnagogic state. A parapsychologist might reply that the hypnagogic state and intense yearning were simply the necessary steps that eventually allowed the bereaved to see beyond the physical world, and glimpse the spiritual realms.

I feel we are each entitled to enjoy the right to our own faith (so long as we do not relinquish that right by forcing our faith on others): the universe is large enough to accommodate a great many points of view, some of which are bound to be diametrically opposed. While science is far from explaining all the experiences people report, it does shed a welcome light on a great many mysteries that were previously the exclusive province of occultism and religion.

A thousand years ago angels and demons stalked the earth watching people's every move; fifty years ago extraterrestrial aliens were arriving in droves; now in the first decade of the twenty-first century we are discovering new techniques to understand the power of the human mind. Who knows what future generations may discover?

Like most people, I have experienced phenomena that fall within the remit of modern parapsychology (everyday oddities such as déjà-vu, bizarre coincidences, beginner's luck, nightmare, to name just a few of the commoner sorts), but I've always been more interested in finding out more about them, rather than merely shoe-horning them into a fashionable or convenient theory. You could call me open minded, but that would leave me vulnerable to wry observations such as "if you keep your mind open too long your brains leak out"; or to paraphrase the arch wit Groucho Marx "you've got an open mind, I can feel the draught from here!"

Although the truth about many sorts of paranormal phenomena is unknown, and might even be ultimately unknowable, I have found the witnesses themselves to be generally reliable and honest, and at pains to relate their experiences accurately. It is often the case that simply for *ease of expression* people talk in terms of spirits and ghosts when trying to describe their encounters: we should remember the acronym UFO stands for *Unidentified* Flying Object.

Paranormal phenomena have been experienced all around the world and throughout history. Indeed, with such supernatural beings as gods and angels rightly included in this broad field of study, the sheer number of people with religious convictions based on their own personal experiences means that 'the paranormal' is really the norm...

Ken Taylor

CHAPTER ONE

SHADOWS of THE PAST

 HERE IS NO MORE DIRECT LINK WITH THE PAST THAN SEEING A GHOST, AND THE DARTMOUTH AREA — ALREADY RENOWNED FOR ITS RICH HISTORY AND HERITAGE of EARLY ARCHITECTURE — offers GENEROUS OPPORTUNITIES FOR SUPERNATURAL SIGHTSEEING.

Many of the places included in this chapter are open to the public, and none of these ghosts have demonstrated a desire to communicate with any of the witnesses, which makes them ideal subjects for newcomers to the art of ghost-watching. They can still be frightening, as we shall see soon enough, but unlike poltergeists, which we shall encounter in the next chapter, they have not been known actually to interfere with anybody.

Their complete lack of interaction with witnesses is such a notable characteristic of this sort of ghost that they actually appear as lifeless as a shadow. Indeed, it is perfectly appropriate to use the poetic term 'shade' to describe this class of haunting because, just as our bodies cast our shadow across space, these long-dead individuals seem to have cast their image across time.

GHOSTLY FERRY PASSENGER

In honour of the immortal Charon, who tirelessly ferries the souls of the dead across the river Styx to the Greek underworld, we should begin our adventures with the ghost on the ferry crossing between Kingswear and Dartmouth. The ghost of an old woman has been seen so often on the Passenger Ferry, that James Thomas calls her the Grey Granny.

The bridge at Old Mill Creek, Dartmouth (see pages 18,48,94).

He first saw her in the early autumn of 2001, when he was skipper of the ferry, but he has heard of sightings since the early 1990s, and she was seen as recently as 2005. "It doesn't matter which boat or time of year," he told me. "But it was always a quiet time of day, usually in the afternoon."

She doesn't call attention to herself; she's small, under five feet (1.5m) in height, and whoever is working on the ferry barely notices her, but assumes she's an ordinary passenger. The haunting usually starts when someone aboard the Passenger Ferry catches a glimpse of her midway down the ramp of Kingswear pontoon, which is what James himself saw. Although she has never been seen clearly, he thinks she may have been wearing a coat like a grey anorak.

He recalls saying to his deckhand "Just wait until this old lady's on, and we'll go." Onboard were James, a deckhand, two hikers and the old lady. "But," he said. "We got to Dartmouth and realised the old lady wasn't there."

In October 2005 a deckhand saw her on the Kingswear Pontoon. James told me "It was blowing a gale and raining. The ferry was coming in to land, and he noticed a head bobbing down the pontoon, as if someone was in a hurry. Then he saw the torso and recognised the figure as that of a lady. He opened the gate to let her on board, but there was nobody there."

Despite the wind and rain, the weather was unseasonably mild, which is notable because when the deckhand walked up the ramp he found that the whole middle section felt as cold as ice. He described it as being like going through a slicer — first his nose and then his forehead felt the shock of the freezing temperature, then his body and legs as he walked into what seemed like a deep freeze. This continued for about twenty feet (6m), and he came out the other side in the same abrupt way.

James added that in 2004 the ferry crew were so certain a woman had been on board that they called the Brixham Coastguard because they were afraid she had gone overboard.

I raised the idea that perhaps exactly that scenario had once occurred and she had indeed drowned (hauntings of the shade type, sometimes seem to be initiated by tragic circumstances), but James pointed out that she has been seen on several different ferry boats, which points towards a different interpretation: "It's not the boat that's haunted," he said, "but the crossing."

One explanation I've heard is that she had intended making the crossing — and it may have been important or urgent that she did so — but she was prevented from embarking. So she has become caught in a sort of loop in time, and is continually attempting to complete the journey she failed to make in life. I'm not really in the business of speculating about what ghosts may or may not be, but I think the ferrymen would have noticed if an old lady had been anxious or agitated, so I prefer a different interpretation. What if her last thoughts were of a little voyage she had always loved, and her happy memories are somehow imprinted on the place? Perhaps when a ferry happens to be in the right place at the right time, her spirit may become visible for a while.

spirits of stone and mortar

It may seem surprising at first, but it is important to realise that not only human beings seem able to cast their image or shadow through time, animals and even inanimate objects can do so too, as the following story from the Slapton area reveals.

The hamlet of Start lies at the end of the road for normal traffic, but an ancient green lane (once a packhorse route to Kingsbridge) leads away towards the west — to Battle Ford and then up to Harleston. Several witnesses have reported hearing the sounds of galloping horses reverberating along the old road, but the creatures causing such commotion have remained invisible to human eyes. Some of these witnesses lived at Start House, a substantial Georgian building, later occupied by a woman who contacted well-known Devonshire folklorist Theo Brown about an even more bizarre event.[1]

One misty afternoon in November 1939 she and her visiting sister went for a stroll along the lane, and they paused to admire the view from a gate. As they gazed across the steeply sloping valley they saw a grand mansion or manor house nestling amongst some trees in the fields on the Harleston side — a spot where she had never seen a building before, although she had lived there for a year and knew the area well.

They watched with mounting astonishment for five minutes, and noticed as outbuildings appeared around it. But, although every detail was clear and distinct — they particularly noticed the large arch of the manor's main doors — all these structures seemed to lack substance and solidity. Then everything faded away and disappeared.

The next year she went with her husband to examine the site (their husbands had both been away in the war at the time of the sighting) and noted that there seemed to be a level platform where the house had been seen to stand. The grass there was also of a different sort to that commonly found in the surrounding fields. The map for 1889[2] does indeed show the site of a manor, already no longer standing, in a wooded field or orchard near Battle Ford at Harleston.

---

[1] Theo Brown 1982, *Devon Ghosts*, Norwich, Jarrold & Sons.
[2] Ordnance Survey 1889, County series. The site lies at grid reference OSGB SX 795451 (this and later grid references are taken from the 1:25,000 scale map: Ordnance Survey 2005, *Explorer OL20 South Devon*, Edition B1, Southampton, Ordnance Survey).

It was not long before the assumption arose that the ghostly horses heard near Start House actually belonged to the stables of the phantom manor at Harleston. Battle Ford, incidentally, is so-called because the area is traditionally regarded as the scene of 9th century battle between the Saxons and Danes.[3] Mrs Jane Ashby, owner of Start House in 2006 told me that although cannonballs had been found in the vicinity, they clearly post-dated that battle. She also added that, in the almost forty years she has lived there, there had been nothing ghostly to report about the house.

If Slapton lies near the southern extreme of Dartmouth's hinterland then about 7 miles (11 km) away, Cornworthy lies at its northernmost limit. Cornworthy used to host a priory of Augustinian nuns, but nothing now remains above ground apart from the isolated and ruined gatehouse (see front cover). This massive thirteenth century edifice would form an imposing portal to any ghost story, and a procession of ghostly nuns has reportedly been seen nearby. But rumour suggests the sighting included parts of the priory buildings, which were long ago reduced to mere grassy mounds in a field. If true, even a sketch could be of great benefit to archaeologists and architectural historians.

WHEN WALLS ARE DOORS

Sandy Holman told me a charming tale about Agincourt House, 27 Lower Street, which is reputed to be Dartmouth's second oldest building and was included in a list compiled in 1380 (so it must have changed its original name to commemorate the famous Battle of Agincourt in 1415). In those days, Lower Street was on the waterfront and, naturally, the house has been altered over the centuries: most recently it has been known as The Merchant's Table restaurant. Sandy saw a ghost here on two occasions, and each time the ghost did "exactly the same thing", which indicates it may be bound by the supernatural laws that seem to govern shades.

The first of her experiences occurred around 9 or 10 o'clock one evening in June 2004, Sandy was sitting at her favourite table near the window on the ground floor. She was chatting with the owner of the establishment when she suddenly fell silent, put her hand to her face, and exclaimed: "There's a ghost."

Her companion asked: "Where?"

"Right behind you!"

She watched as the figure of a woman appeared to come through the wall. The ghost took a couple of steps into the room and if Sandy had reached out her hand she could have touched her, yet Sandy insists the apparition was not scary. "She was dressed in a long grey dress with a white apron and white cap, so she could have been a servant. She just came out and looked right at me, and stood there for a moment or two, and then walked backward into the wall. Still looking at me, she faded away through the wall.

---

[3] Valerie Belsey 2003, *Exploring Green Lanes in the South Hams*, Totnes, Green Books.

Agincourt House, Dartmouth (see pages 14-16,20,50).

"She didn't frighten me at all," Sandy emphasised. "She had a nice mouth with a half smile, and was very serene and attractive. She looked around thirty years old, slim, and about five feet four inches tall."

The table where Sandy sat was not the first inside the main entrance but was set to the left of it. She was, as was her habit, sitting facing the front window: to her right-hand side beside the table was a large upright wooden black beam that stands the full height of the wall. The ghost appeared to come through the old wall immediately to the right hand side of that pillar, which is where a doorway originally existed.

Sandy saw her ghost again about six weeks later. It was at the same time of evening and Sandy was sitting at the same table, and the spirit repeated her movements precisely. While this series of similarities suggests that this haunting replays one particular incident over and over again, we must take note of Sandy's remark that the woman seemed to look right at her.

Taken at face value, if the ghost did indeed see Sandy, then we could suppose that the ghost managed to somehow pass through a door that not only led into a different room but into the 21st century. How such a woman might peer so far into the future yet remain so calm mystifies me unless she was a talented natural clairvoyant accustomed to seeing strange and fascinating sights. The mind boggles at what else she may have discovered about the world of the supernatural, but sadly I have discovered no record of a 'white witch' in the area.

However, we cannot ignore the fact that this ghost failed to make any sign of recognition when she met Sandy the second time (or even, just in case her jumps through time were not in the same order that Sandy experienced them, the first time). So perhaps Sandy was simply occupying exactly the same position as something on which the ghost had once fixed her attention, a century or more ago. Perhaps Sandy's presence at that precise spot even helped to trigger the return of this charming manifestation.

There is, however, a tantalising alternative to the common idea that buildings act like psychic video recorders, replaying old images in an endless loop. Imagine for a moment that, instead of the ghostly manifestation projecting forwards into our time, we could actually somehow glance backwards and glimpse the past through a suddenly opened window in time. In either case these particular ghosts remain unconscious of our presence.

On balance I felt the case was sufficiently strong to place this story in this chapter rather than the next — I prefer to think of the woman's appearances as a repeating haunting of the shade variety rather than two visits by a conscious spirit. But should Sandy or anyone else see her again I wouldn't be surprised to hear of further developments.

This ghost may even have been the same that materialised right beside a customer, and vanished as swiftly as it appeared, in the 1980s when Agincourt House was an antique shop. The voices of children were also heard, when it was impossible for anyone to be there, during that period.

MoRE DOORS of paranormaL peRcEptIoN

A serene smile can really lift our spirits, and the occasion is made even more memorable if we discover we may have been greeted by a ghost. Another incident of a woman in a doorway was described to me by Heri, who was employed in the kitchen at the Royal Castle Hotel, 11 The Quay, Dartmouth. He told me that at about 9pm on a busy weekend, a few weeks after he came to work at the hotel in April 2004, he went up to a staff room on the top floor, and saw a woman standing holding open the fire exit door at the back of the building. He said she was wearing the normal uniform of the housekeeping staff — blue trousers and with a blue apron (the uniform has been changed slightly since then).

He said "Hi" as she smiled at him, and thought nothing of it as he turned into the room. A minute or so later he came back out into the hall, and she was still there; he was just a yard or so (1m) away from her. She was standing with her left arm against the door, holding it open, and she appeared to be about 35 to 40 years old, with long, curly blonde hair that nearly reached down to her waist. They exchanged smiles, and he went back along the short hall towards the central stairwell. Heri, a friendly and courteous young man, turned a few seconds later to bid her a final farewell as he left the hallway, but she was no longer there — the door was shut and she had vanished.

Heri mentioned her to his boss, the head chef, but he didn't recognise her from Heri's description, and he also agreed it was unusual to have housekeepers working so late. Heri never saw her again, and in the eighteen months since seeing this mystery woman, he has never met any of the housekeepers there. But what really puzzled him, and made the hairs on the nape of his neck stand on end when he told me the story, was that the fire exit has a complex mechanism that makes a loud and distinct clatter as the door closes securely — yet she had disappeared without a sound.

Across the water, the Royal Dart at Kingswear was once the Great Western Hotel, but now the hotel's guest rooms upstairs have been converted into private flats. A couple of years ago, a woman who lived there told James Thomas that her flat was haunted. He told me that she had "been woken up at one or two in the morning by a Victorian lady walking through the bedroom. She had appeared in the doorway, stared at the resident where she was lying in bed, then walked away through a wall where a doorway used to be." This happened several times.

This event has a clear hallmark of the 'recording' type of phenomenon — walking through a doorway that no longer exists is a classic trait of this sort of haunting. But, as in the Agincourt House case, the way the Victorian lady seemed to look at the woman in the bed could indicate an ability to take notice of and react to events in the 'here-and-now' — the sign of a sentient ghost. Perhaps the owner of the flat just happened to be in part of the room that once caught the attention of the lady in the Victorian era, a coincidence that may have somehow triggered the replay. Perhaps a course of action as simple as moving the bed could end a haunting such as this.

We need to travel exactly five miles (8 km) to the east, to the village of Blackawton, for our final example of a woman in a doorway. Ursula Dimes, who lived there for many years, told me she had known "two young girls, about fourteen years old, who saw the figure of a farmer's wife in the [St Michael's] church porch." The problem was that the woman had died not long before.

"They weren't lying," she added. "They ran away!"

a blue nun's smile

Old Mill Creek is situated just upstream from Dartmouth, on the west side of the Dart: it is set in a secluded, wooded valley, and at dawn on a summer's day the rising sun's warming light streams along the stretch of mirror-bright water. Terry Pritchard habitually visited the end of the Creek at low tide to gather ragworms for fishing bait and, on one summer morning around 1975 in the half hour after 4:30am, he become aware of a nun standing to the right of the bridge at the end of the creek. He said hello and, in the time it took to light a cigarette, she had unaccountably managed to move clear around to the left of him and now stood watching him from the grassy shore.

He observed her closely and noticed her habit consisted of a grey skirt, blue top and wimple (with a white band at the front), and buckled shoes. She was smiling, wore spectacles, and had wooden beads and a wooden cross around her neck, and there was a chain around her waist from which something was dangling. Then she simply "vaporised." The whole incident took no more than 60 seconds. (The sketch is by Iris, Terry's wife, and was painstakingly drawn to his approval.)

Not long after, when Terry was heading down to the Creek from Dartmouth, he rounded the sharp bend near the bridge and saw the nun walking uphill towards him. This time she seemed to be in all black and white. As they passed each other he looked into her face but saw only "greyness" in place of any human features.

For a week he saw nothing but then, this time in the company of his son (who was about nine years old), he saw her on the road again. He asked his son "Can you see anything?" but he couldn't. As soon as they'd passed her, Terry looked back but she had vanished. For about a week after this he saw the same black and white figure every morning.

As with the hauntings we have discussed above, there is some doubt whether this ghost truly belongs in this or the next chapter. The fact that Terry Pritchard thought she looked at him on the first occasion argues she was aware of him but, as with the other reports, perhaps his presence at that spot helped to trigger the haunting to re-enact a moment when the nun was watching something or somebody else. Again, the lack of positive reaction to him on subsequent sightings inclines me to provisionally classify this manifestation as a shade.

Little more than half a mile (0.8km) away ghostly nuns have also been seen in the vicinity of Mount Boone, Dartmouth, very close to the site of the medieval chapel of St Clare that once overlooked the harbour from its vantage point on the lower half of what is now Clarence Hill. It may be worth noting that some members of the Franciscan order of Poor Clare are among several orders of nuns who do not wear the conventional black habit but, in honour of the Virgin Mary, wear blue.

The smiling nun of Old Mill Bridge (see page 10).

CHURCH MONKS

Ghostly monks have been seen in the area around the Civil War fort of Gallants Bower, and along Castle Road. They are thought to be associated with the old chapel that was the precursor to the church of St Petrox adjacent to Dartmouth Castle.

Other monks have been seen near the church of St Saviour (Anzac Street, Dartmouth), which was consecrated in 1372, but before considering them we may note in passing that for some years in the 1970s shrieks and other grisly noises were regularly heard emanating from the churchyard after midnight mass each Christmas Eve — becoming known as the Phantom of St Saviour's. Such spectacularly eerie and undoubtedly entertaining events are not uncommon, and students of the paranormal usually assign them to pranksters and natural high spirits rather than supernatural sources.

More decorously though, as befits the interior of this place of worship, local people have noticed a man sitting in one of the front pews, praying; only to find that when they look around again he has unaccountably disappeared. By all accounts his clothes place him to the mid 20th century. Another manifestation in the church is that of a figure seen in or around 1968, apparently lying in an aisle on the memorial dedicated to Mr Fox.

There is also a long-standing but unsubstantiated local tradition that a long-forgotten tunnel leads from this church into one of the old houses close-by in Smith Street. The house to which the ancient passage leads is, so the story goes, haunted by monks clad in dark coloured robes, rumoured to be guardians of a precious secret that was hidden and then lost in centuries past.

ELIZABETHAN GHOSTS

One evening in 2004, in the upper restaurant at Agincourt House, executive chef Lloyd Scribbins had a memorable experience. He told me "I saw the figure of a bloke in a sort of Elizabethan tunic (no ruff) with pantaloons. He was bending down to use the fireplace as if to light a long clay pipe. Then he disappeared."

Another site with an 'Elizabethan' ghost is also one of the most haunted places in Dartmouth: The Spinning Wheel Tea Rooms in Hauley Road. It is another of those buildings listed in the local gazetteer of 1380, and is justly famed as one of the oldest and most appealing tea rooms in the Southwest.

Around 1965, at about 7:00 or 7:30 on a quiet evening in the summer season, manageress Frances Cawthorne was washing tea towels alone in the kitchen. "The back door was always open" she told me, adding she "saw a figure standing there watching me. She had a bundle in her arms. She was wearing a cape and was rather greyish looking, and a little on the plump side."

Mrs Cawthorne wanted to call her husband to come to see it, but she felt that any disturbance would make the spirit vanish. Moments later the ghost did indeed simply disappear as if she had walked through the door and into some invisible dimension, leaving the witness somewhat shocked but not frightened.

Mrs Cawthorne also told me about one of her waitresses who also had a ghostly experience whilst working alone in the kitchen early in the 1970s. She heard the front door open and assumed a customer had entered; she distinctly heard him wrestle off an oilskin, which seemed to be heavy and stiff like an old-fashioned type. But although the waitress's service was as prompt as could be, there was not a soul to be seen. It is rumoured that he was Welynton, leader of the Dartmouth Privateers, who owned the premises some 500 or so years ago; if true, this would make him the most ancient of all the apparitions known in the town.

In the early 1980s, when Joan Bacon had taken over as manager, a customer reported seeing the ghost of a man with exceptionally angular features. Even his beard was pointed and slightly crescent shaped. He wore a bi- or tri-corn hat (predominantly an 18th century fashion), and peered through a doorway from one tea room into an adjoining one nearer the front door.

Around the same time another customer saw the ghosts of a mother and child walk right past and enter the same room from which the angular man had stared out. Was this perhaps another sighting of the woman with the bundle, seen by Frances Cawthorne?

Although neither Paula Bell nor her husband, managers of the Tea Rooms since 2001, have seen any ghosts themselves, she did mention that some guests reported vague but friendly psychic impressions after hearing about the ghosts, particularly those who sat in 'the haunted room'. She explained that the ghost of an Elizabethan man sits there: he is affectionately called George, but hasn't actually been seen for decades. If you'd like to visit the haunted room, it's the one on the left as you enter from the courtyard, up a step, and at the far end. With the spice of mystery sprinkled over it, The Spinning Wheel Tea Rooms certainly enjoys a unique atmosphere that is hard to define yet easy to enjoy.

CHERUBIC SPIRITS

From what may be the oldest ghosts in Dartmouth (much older ghosts will be found in the hinterland in the next chapter) we may now consider what is thought to be the oldest building in the town. The Cherub, 13 Higher Street, is Dartmouth's last remaining complete medieval house: it was built for a wealthy wool merchant some time before 1380, and is currently a popular public house and restaurant. This street was the town's main high street, and not so long ago it was as crammed with ancient buildings as a modern mall is brimful of shops.

The name 'Cherub' does not refer to one of those magical creatures that are the living powers of a deity whose name, when uttered correctly, can reputedly destroy the universe; neither does it relate to some sentimental Victorian's caricature of Cupid. The name simply refers to a type of seafaring vessel, apt considering Dartmouth is one of Devonshire's most ancient ports.

While some shades remain active for centuries, most seem to grow fainter with time and may cease after just a few years or decades; and some hauntings that were current in The Cherub when I lived in Dartmouth in the 1980s seem to have already faded into obscurity. In 2005 I met Mrs Margaret Lawson who has worked at the restaurant for many years, and she told me that although there is still a rumour of a ghost haunting the table by the fireplace in the upstairs restaurant, she hadn't heard anything of the other traditional ghosts for years.

In the early 1980s the figure of an ashen-haired old lady was seen on several occasions sitting quietly beside the fireplace in the public bar on the ground floor. Presumably it was once her favoured spot for to warm herself in front of the comfortable blaze, which reminds us that it is not only tragic or heart-stopping crises that are commemorated in hauntings (mind you, we are in no position to judge what matters occupied her thoughts). However, twenty years later, the story of the ghost in the alcove by the fireplace referred not to our 'grey lady' but to an old man wreathed in sweet-smelling pipe smoke. I suspect this to be a case of Chinese Whispers in which one original story changes a little bit each time it is passed from person to person, but perhaps there really are two ghosts.

It is often reported that animals sense ghosts even when people don't, and this seems to have been the case with an Old English Sheepdog called William. Late one evening in 1982 he watched an invisible 'someone', presumed to be our grey-haired ghost, cross slowly from the foot of the stairs to the fireplace. William simply sat and stared with no sign of alarm, which proves it wasn't the resident cat spirit (below). However, the man who witnessed this uncharacteristic canine behaviour was not so sanguine, and hastily left the scene.

The next tale is one of my personal favourites: a black cat is reputed to haunt the stairs between the ground floor and the first. In view of how steep and twisting these stairs are, such a good luck mascot should be regarded as a useful ally, but at least two previous owners have fallen foul of this impish creature getting under their feet. The first of these, a manager of the pub, failed to inform his successor about the cat, and the latter nearly trod on the beastie near the bottom of the stairs. He stumbled but didn't fall, but the tray of glasses he was carrying crashed down to the floor. Believing it to be a 'real' animal he mounted a thorough search of the premises, much to the amusement of the regulars who knew all about the traditional story.

The Cherub has a 'burglar stair' with a step whose riser is of a different height to the rest, which is designed to trip nocturnal intruders. That, coupled with the idea that a fleeting glimpse of a dark shape on a shadowy staircase could be nothing but a trick of the eye, may explain the manager's accident, but the story of the phantom puss remains a delightful way to remind people to take care on the stairs — *beware of the cat.*

THE CIVIL WAR AND OTHER HORRORS

We need not stray far from The Cherub to find some more of the town's oldest ghosts: Cavaliers. In 1642 at the start of the English Civil War, Dartmouth declared for Parliament, but the following year Cavaliers, the Royalist supporters of King Charles I, mounted a month-long siege and took the town in early October. The ghost of a Cavalier was seen a little to the east of The Cherub in 1967 at one of the modern buildings that line the western side of Higher Street.

Not far across town is an equally prosperous street, Duke Street, which boasts the fabulous Butterwalk (see page 95) that would have been less than ten years old when the Cavaliers occupied the town. This spectacular row of timber-framed houses dates from 1628 to 1640, and has granite pillars with carved capitals supporting its upper storeys above the pavement. The Jacobean façade, which was damaged by bombing in WW2 but restored in 1954, is adorned with elaborately carved woodwork depicting, among other eye-catching motifs, half-human-half-animal hybrids and a variety of mythical beasts.

Upstairs at 12 Duke Street is the so-called Jesse Room, in which a ghostly Cavalier has been seen standing beside the fireplace. There is a hint that he was a devout man as he most frequently manifested on Sundays, and the room itself is celebrated for its religious mouldings: its exceptional ceiling displays the Tree of Jesse, which represents the ancestry of Jesus traced through the Virgin Mary to Jesse, father of King David, a lineage that fulfils a Biblical prophesy.[4]

The occupying Royalist forces built a fort between 1643 and 1646 — Gallant's Bower. It held a strategically important position overlooking Weeke valley and Dartmouth Castle but fell to the lord general of the Parliamentary forces, Sir Thomas Fairfax at the cost of many lives in January 1646. The fort's well-preserved earthworks have seen substantial restoration in the past decade.

A short way to the northwest of the fort is a woodland area that is literally carpeted with bluebells in late spring. In this so-called Bluebell Glade in 1980, a local woman encountered a headless horseman, a frightening spectacle that may be connected with the battle that had raged through this now tranquil beauty spot. The ghosts of more conventional Cavaliers have been seen around the fort itself and along Castle Road.

To the north of the Gallant's Bower ridge rises Dyer's Hill, and the valley between runs down to Warfleet. Late one night in the summer of 1982, a visitor from the North Country was walking along the old road out of Dartmouth that nestles in this vale

---

[4] Isaiah chapter 11.

(Weeke Hill), and must have had the shock of his life when he also saw that most celebrated of clichéd phantoms, the headless horseman.

Another incident on Weeke Hill occurred around midnight on Whitsuntide 1980 (Whitsunday was May 25th), when Philip Law, a visitor from the Midlands, was walking up the hill away from the town. "I had gone past the houses on the right and then past a farm gate on the left. I was somewhere between the farm gate and the small road a bit further up the hill on the left." Just then he saw a figure of at least average height, walking along the road ahead of him.

"I thought it may have been one of my friends who had gone on ahead about half an hour earlier... Before I could catch him up he just was not there anymore and I had an urge to look behind me and saw him in the distance, and I think there was some thing by or behind the farm gates that was not there when I passed. I then ran up the hill because this was a disturbing situation to be in and I wanted to get away as fast as possible." He told me "I am not exactly sure how the figure disappeared but it obviously frightened me."

Weeke Hill has a strong reputation as a haunted road, and local people interpreted Philip's story as another sighting of 'The Coachman', referring to Dartmouth's most famous and well-documented haunting: the ghostly coach of The Royal Castle Hotel.

hotel's 300-year-old royal guest?

The main haunting at The Royal Castle Hotel, Dartmouth, is usually described as a repeating manifestation that was generated over 300 years ago by an event combining romance and royalty in a dramatic historical setting.[5] But it is a tale with a twist...

On Monday November 5th, 1688 (so the story goes), the coaching inn was host to the 26-year-old daughter of James II, Princess Mary. Her visit was filled with anxiety while she awaited the arrival of her husband William of Orange, who planned to sail into Dartmouth with 400 ships and an army of 15,000 men to seize her father's throne. She was a poor sailor and had left the Netherlands ahead of this armada (coincidentally on the centenary of the Spanish) to take advantage of calm weather before the winter winds began. Her stay in Dartmouth was fairly safe as the Southwest was generally against King James II, and was happy to support Prince William's claim.

---

[5] This story can be found, for example, in Andrew Green's 1973 book *Our Haunted Kingdom,* London, Wolfe Publishing; A Farquharson-Coe 1974 (rev 1975), *Devon's Ghosts,* St Ives, James Pike; Ralph Whitlock 1977, *The Folklore of Devon,* London, Batsford; Judy Chard 1979, *Devon Mysteries,* Bodmin, Bossiney Books; Peter Underwood 1982, *Ghosts of Devon,* Bodmin, Bossiney Books; Guy Lyon Playfair 1985, *The Haunted Pub Guide,* London, Harrap; and Sally & Chips Barber 1995, *Haunted Pubs in Devon,* Exeter, Obelisk Publications. It is also retold on many websites.

Bad weather not only delayed William's fleet by a day but forced it to shelter in Tor Bay. As soon as the prince landed in Brixham harbour to the anticipated friendly welcome, he despatched a messenger to ride by way of Totnes Bridge, bearing tidings of his safe anchorage, and instructions for Mary to ready herself for a carriage that would carry her to meet him. It seems that the messenger arrived in the dead of night: the clattering of hooves that marked his hasty entry into the inn is still often heard echoing through time. These ghostly sounds are loudest in the hotel's central courtyard and reception area, which used to lead into the old courtyard and stables to the rear (now occupied by an upholstery business).

Now, as in 1688, his noisy arrival is the herald of an even greater commotion. After the noise of the lone horseman has passed, the rumble of wheels crunching over cobbles is heard as an invisible spectral carriage rattles into the long-gone courtyard. Footsteps pound, doors open and slam shut again, the team of horses is whipped up, and the princess and her ladies-in-waiting embark on the journey to reunite the couple destined to ascend to the throne of Britain. As the vehicle departs, the church bell is heard tolling two o'clock, and the haunting is at an end, for another year at least.

A local man who we shall call John worked at the Royal Castle Hotel for a while in about 1991, and he told me he once heard the phantom carriage. He gave me (if I may coin the phrase) this ear-witness account. It was late one November and John was on the first floor in the walk-in freezer, which was situated directly above the reception area.

He first noticed "a very low rumble, then discerned the sound of horses' hooves and creaky wheels over cobble stones. It sounded like it was coming from underneath me. I could hear the squeaking as it stopped out the back where the stables were, and a door opened on the carriage. I heard voices, muffled; and creaking like somebody stepping out — the springs on one side of the carriage.

"I went to a window overlooking the back of the hotel, and lifted it open and looked outside... Nothing. The voices stopped abruptly; suddenly like I'd pressed 'Stop' on a tape recorder."

Then he heard St Saviour's church bell toll twice — 2am.

The prince's army found no fight left in James II, so he travelled to London without mishap (apparently haunting a room in Forde House, Newton Abbot along the way). There, in 1689, Parliament declared the happy couple to be King William III and Queen Mary II. It is notable that this whole affair revolves around a spiritual struggle: James II was an ardent Catholic, whereas Mary and William were both staunch Protestants (it is a remarkable legacy of this religious conflict that to this day, the reigning monarch cannot be or even be married to a Catholic).

Another clue perhaps, as to how Mary's sojourn could have generated enough emotional energy to leave an impression strong enough to last more than 300 years, lies in the date of the events. Had not the hostile weather delayed the prince's landing, the couple's reunion would have coincided with his birthday (November 4th), which was also the date of their wedding anniversary. We can imagine her languishing in autumnal Dartmouth, with an uncertain military campaign ahead of her, as the expected happy anniversary reunion failed to materialise.

Regrettably, the supernatural events have an equally exasperating inability to commemorate exact dates: it is most often heard in October by guests and staff alike (including the former manager, Mrs Gwyneth Powell who heard it as early as 1950, and many times thereafter) but sometimes in November or late September.

the twist in the tale

The touchstone of romance certainly adds to this ghost story's undying appeal. Unfortunately, and here's the twist, this story has been roundly discredited in an excellent little book by Ray Freeman.[6] She gives several reasons why this version of events could not have taken place. Firstly, Mary did not arrive in advance of William's military campaign — she followed him when the throne was safely won the following spring. Secondly, the roads around Dartmouth were so poor that although packhorses could use them, no carriage could have done so. And finally, the Royal Castle Hotel simply did not exist then — it was still two private houses owned by local merchants, and didn't become an inn until the following century.

The ease with which this myth has been exploded by some competent historical research highlights how important it is for would-be investigators into the paranormal to check the facts behind a traditional story — however often it has appeared in print. But, just in case I have ever fallen foul of a similar oversight, may I to call to mind the proverb that suggests erring is human whilst forgiving is divine; and commend any author of good faith into your hands — be critical but not cruel.

Ray Freeman is kind enough to offer an alternative source for the noises that have been so frequently reported. She suggests that if the origin is supernatural then perhaps they emanate from the scene of a mysterious death: that of William Tabb who worked with the horses in the stable at the rear of the hotel. He was found one morning in 1895, drowned in the horse trough. The doors to the stable yard were locked, yet there was no telling precisely how he came to his death; the presumption was that he was the victim of a tragic accident. There is a local traditional still circulating that the ghost of his body can sometimes be seen in the phantom trough, with his legs dangling over the side.

---

[6] Ray Freeman 1998, *The History of The Castle Hotel Dartmouth*, Dartmouth, Dartmouth History Research Group.

Coincidentally perhaps, the hotel is indeed said to be the long-term home of an ostler. Darkie Chase lived over the stables, and his ghost has been seen on several occasions on his way downstairs. Witnesses have described him as being lightly built and small in stature.

That the hotel's stables were packed with incident may or may not be related to the phantom coach (even if Mary wasn't the passenger, this repeating haunting surely indicates that somebody had the ride of their lives), the vehicle seems to have left a trail of manifestations across the town — and maybe beyond. Although the pacing steeds that draw the carriage are rarely seen, the racket they raise is frequently heard careering away from The Quay. The phantom carriage heads up Smith Street, and along Higher Street (and, again, a lone horseman has been heard here preceding the carriage, briefly lingering outside The Cherub), and then it continues its rattling journey via Southtown to Warfleet Road and Weeke Hill.

We cannot be sure whether or not it is connected with Dartmouth's famous carriage, but a ghostly coach had also been heard at The London Inn at Dartmouth Road, Stoke Fleming, which suggests the vehicle was on the route between Dartmouth and Kingsbridge. In the mid 19th century travellers enjoyed a regular and reliable service along this route — three times a week.

The only known sighting of Dartmouth's coach-and-four occurred at Weeke Hill and was witnessed by a visitor to the town who was unaware of the context of his experience. Three of the four horses appeared distinctly unhealthy and grey in hue, the fourth (on the outside left) was bay with markings that struck him as somehow unnatural.

While we're on the subject of phantom animals, we should briefly consider the Clink Horse, one of Dartmouth's traditional supernatural entities. It is never seen, only heard, its metal shoes ringing on cobbles that no longer exist. Mind you, there are still ancient cobbles on the quay near the early 16th century fort at Bayards Cove, and these too have rung with the metallic clattering of shoes belonging to invisible horses, sounds that were heard by two witnesses together. Also, a phantom dog has been seen haunting an alley not far from Bayards Cove, near Agincourt House: to my knowledge it was last seen on Monday December 21st, 1981.

However, we may now return to the Royal Castle Hotel, which not only boasts the most famous haunting, but also seems to be the most haunted place in town. In the mid 1980s I had the pleasure of meeting local resident Mrs Perring who told me about an experience she had one Easter shortly after the First World War. She was working at the hotel at the time, and saw a "gentleman" with fair, shoulder-length hair, and a friendly face. She remembered him vividly, and said he wore a maroon coloured coat, a shirt with lace on the cuffs, and a white cravat. Suddenly though, with his hand still on the banister of the stairs, he simply disappeared right in front of her. Later she found out that the hotel chef had also seen him some time before.

When John was working at the hotel, an elderly lady who was staying in Room 22 on the top floor, came rushing downstairs in her nightdress; she was as white as a sheet, prompting the receptionist to exclaim — ironically as it turned out — "You look like you've seen a ghost!"

Her astonishing tale was quickly told: she had seen a young girl floating outside her bedroom window — the window in this room opens onto a sheer drop into the stairwell or atrium. She absolutely refused to go back to stay in the room, and had to be found alternative accommodation. This, the third floor, is not part of the original building, but was added in about 1840 when the proprietor was looking to expand and aptly decided 'the only way is up'.

An unexplained light near the ceiling of Room 22.

John added that other people have reported the pungent smell of very strong sailors' tobacco in that room, although no source or smoke was visible. (Incidentally, a similar smell has been noticed near but not actually in the Dartmouth Museum at The Butterwalk.)

It was this very room that I was given when I arrived in 2005 as the guest of the hotel's proprietor Nigel Way. I have detailed some of my experiences there in the next chapter, but here I should mention that the first thing I did upon taking possession of the room was to photograph it from all angles. Nothing struck me as unusual until I had the pictures developed. One of the prints shows a distinct yellow fuzzy blob of light that seems to hang in the air to the right hand side near the ceiling. I was certainly not aware of it when I took the photo.[7]

I showed the print and negative to photographer Adrian Good who began his professional career in the early 1970s photographing television and radio personalities for ITV, and has a wide range of expertise in the subject, and he confessed that it puzzled him. In all his years of experience he had never seen anything quite like it. He ruled out simple lens flare, and the lens itself was not at fault as the photographs either side were flawless. The only conventional explanation he

---

[7] I used the integral flash of an Olympus Mju-1, with 200 ASA Kodak Colour Plus film.

suggested was a reflection from a highly polished surface somewhere out of frame, which bounced the flash upwards; but the anomaly was extraordinarily bright for that sort of effect. I am not claiming this as 'the ghost of Room 22', but I would file it in the unexplained category until somebody can positively identify it, perhaps by revisiting the room and attempting to replicate the phenomenon.

A 'white lady' wearing a flowing white dress has also been seen, always only briefly, walking along the balcony opposite that room overlooking the central courtyard. Another unusual apparition was seen in the mid 1990s: there were two reports (about a year apart) from the top floor towards the rear of the hotel. In each case a young lady appeared at the foot of the bed saying "Water, water, give me water."

'In or around 1993 he retired to bed after a good meal at the bar, and was clearheaded and sober as he had important business to attend to in the morning. He was awakened by the church bell tolling 1am, and saw what he could best describe as a dark shadow standing at the foot of his bed, its silhouette suggested the figure was wearing a robe. He hastily switched on the light but found he was alone in the room. He has always remembered the event vividly, and was glad of the opportunity of sharing it via Darren's website.

John also told me the tale of the 'phantom night porter' who has been reported several times around the hotel. He knocks on a guests' door, then on the door of the next room, and then the next, working his way along the halls. Guests, believing it to be a fire drill or something similar, have opened their doors but found nobody there.

A real night porter at the hotel told John about his own experience in the first floor Adam Room restaurant in the late 1980s. He was routinely placing fresh candles into the empty wine bottles that served as holders, in readiness for the guests' evening meals, when he heard the unmistakable sounds of a child running around and around the perimeter of the room. Not only was he alone in the room, with a clear view all around him, but heavy tables and chairs were positioned along the walls, making it impossible for anything physical to move quickly around them.

Next to this public room is a room in which staff perform some of the unseen duties that keep the hotel running so smoothly: it was known as the 'Still Room'. Once, when the night porter was downstairs in the bar area, he heard a series of loud crashes and bangs like crockery smashing and pots and pans being thrown around by people having a fight. He ran up immediately but he found nothing was out of place; everything was in perfect order as usual.

---

[8] Devon's section of the searchable list of UK hauntings etc sorted by subject and location may be found at http://www.paranormaldatabase.com/devon/devodata.php [all websites referenced in this book were accessible when the manuscript was finalised in June 2006].

On another occasion, John himself was there at night when all the guests were asleep, and he heard the sound of two men having a heated discussion in the Galleon Bar on the ground floor. He couldn't make out the words, but went in immediately to see what was the matter. The noises fell silent abruptly, and he found the room was completely unoccupied.

Once a building has a reputation as a haunted property, it is easy to imagine how completely spurious anecdotes can arise during barstool conversations. One such example may be the legend that Nell Gwyn still leaves her impression in the bedclothes of the room in which she once stayed. It has even been reported this inn was Charles II's favourite place at which to disentangle himself from unwanted mistresses, and that one may have been made to disappear permanently — and that this is actually the origin of the famous phantom coach.[9]

Such is The Royal Castle Hotel's current reputation however, both for quality of accommodation and for the high level of service the staff afford to their guests, for which I can personally vouch, that I'm sure any visitor would enjoy their stay regardless of which month it happens to be or in which room they sleep.

HIGHWAYMAN IN BLACK

Some way across town, at 7 o'clock in the morning of Friday January 13th (traditionally unlucky for some) 1984, the owner of The Frying Pan, a fish and chip restaurant at 11 Broadstone, descended the stairs into his kitchen as usual. Straight away he noticed it felt chilly, and he checked the window but, as usual, it was securely fastened.

Then he saw the figure of a man wearing what he could only describe as a "highwayman's cape". The ghost was completely dressed in black, right down to his boots. The spectre stood stock-still, barely three yards (2.7m) away, just on the customer's side of the serving bar.

Being a confirmed critic of the occult, the witness told me that he could scarcely believe his eyes. And indeed, when he looked again, the otherworldly customer had vanished.

The same ghost had been seen before: several times at least by the previous owner who remarked that it only ever appeared before dawn. Owner Eddy 'The-Chip' Owens told me that the most recent sighting occurred around 1997 when two customers seated by the front door mentioned to him that "there's a guy there dressed in black." They had seen him behind one of the high-backed seats, but Eddy was positive that the couple themselves had been his first customers that day.

---

[9] Deryck Seymour 1990, *The Ghosts of Torbay*, 32, Exeter, Obelisk Publications.

Like his predecessor, Eddy is not particularly inclined to believe in spirits but told me that around 2am one winter's morning around 1993 he was downstairs in the kitchen when he felt "a dead certain presence behind me." He assumed it was his dog Sheba but when he turned around there was nothing there.

Incidentally, in the same road at number 7, something once spooked Georgina Parker who told me this lovely tale. "When I was a little girl my gran lived there. One day I saw a ghostly figure drift along the landing — but it turned out to be Grandma's lodger — end of mystery!"

a war veteran's suicide

Warfleet Pottery, located at the bottom of Weeke Hill, Dartmouth, is an early 19th century building that has seen a wide variety of activities over the years: it milled grain, became a water-powered paper mill, a brewery, and achieved some degree of fame as Dartmouth Pottery before that business closed in 2002. The property has recently been redeveloped and converted into flats. The ghost is said to be a relic of the period when it was used as a brewery, some time before 1947.

The story goes that a man with military connections hanged himself there, and his spirit haunted the place for a while. Perhaps his suicide was because of the well-known problem of adjusting to civilian life after being demobilised from combat duties (possibly World War Two). I certainly haven't heard of any manifestations in recent decades, so I presume the presence passed on fairly soon, leaving the premises in peace.

D-day: a bad dress-rehearsal

There is a superstition in the theatre that a bad dress-rehearsal is a good omen and indicates that the opening night will be a success; perhaps this also holds true for the theatre of war. At least a major tragedy that occurred off the Slapton coast during the preparations for the D-Day landings at the end of the Second World War, was the forerunner of a bloody but ultimately successful Allied invasion of Nazi-occupied Europe.

Visitors to a guesthouse at nearby Torcross were awakened in the dark of the night by sounds like an approaching storm, yet the late April weather was actually mild. Then they heard gunfire and the screams of men in agony coming from across the beach. The sisters peered out of their window but saw nothing to explain the sounds, but listened in shock to the noise of distant gunfire and screaming out to sea.

It was only when they mentioned it at breakfast that morning that they learned about the off-shore disaster that overtook the D-Day rehearsal on Friday April 28th, 1944. Their hostess particularly remembers the date the sisters mentioned their troubled night — it was the 28th of April.[10]

the oldstone mystery

Stark stone ruins of a once stately building always inspire a powerful emotional response and, in the right light at least, Oldstone Mansion, Blackawton, is an icon of romantic ambiguity. Its now empty walls remind us of an age of grandeur and privilege, yet they present us with a vivid image of the downfall of human aspiration and endeavour. The famous Victorian ghost that haunts the Oldstone estate is certainly a tragic figure, and the manner in which she perished is as much a riddle as the mystery of death itself.

At twenty-two years old, Laura Dimes was the youngest member of the family living at Oldstone and, although her parents were not great socialites, she was an accomplished horsewoman and possessed of an independent spirit. She was certainly capable of a love strong enough to defy the conventions of her times.

Despite her parent's conservative disapproval of an attentive young suitor (he was some five years her senior, and had been involved in enough dubious money-making schemes to make him somewhat disreputable), she made secret plans to be his bride, and on Tuesday April 8th, 1884 she rode to Kingsbridge and married Hugh Shortland by special licence. Unaccountably, instead of eloping together in true romantic style, starting with a honeymoon adventure that could last a lifetime, the groom apparently abandoned poor Laura to remain under her parents' roof, while he immediately embarked on a business trip to New Zealand.

Those must have been difficult days at Oldstone, and they came to a tragic climax on Monday April 28th. Around midday Laura returned from a morning ride, and took her collie dog for a walk — a seemingly ordinary course of events but, although she had changed from riding clothes into a blue day dress, she bizarrely kept wearing her riding gloves and hat. An hour or so later the collie arrived home, and nobody was surprised that it was wet because Laura often played with it around several pools in a nearby dell. But Laura didn't come home.

At dawn the next day a search was undertaken, and her body was found in the higher of the three pools in the grounds. The inquest couldn't decide how she came into the water, and her body was interred after a service in St Saviour's at Dartmouth, at Longcross Cemetery, Townstal, on Saturday May 3rd.

---

[10] Judy Chard 1988 (rev. 1994), *Haunted Happenings in Devon*, Exeter, Obelisk Publications.

To this day speculation continues about her fate — accident, suicide, or murder — because on the Wednesday following the funeral, her widower was discovered hiding at a cottage at Modbury about ten miles (15km) from Oldstone. By his own admission he had not left the area at all, indeed, he claimed he hadn't even left the cottage. Hugh Shortland was promptly arrested on suspicion of murder, but despite compelling circumstantial evidence, the best attentions of a Chief Inspector from Scotland Yard, and an exhumation and post-mortem, no conclusive proof was found to convict him. The trial collapsed and he was acquitted.

That summer, Shortland did leave for New Zealand where, in 1891, he was sentenced to two years imprisonment for libelling a young unmarried woman. The evidence against him included a threat he had made that he would force her to commit suicide — just as he had done to his wife in England.

His intimidating words were one step away from a confession of murder, and that Shortland murdered Laura is the conclusion drawn by local author Carole Thompson whose study of the affair makes absorbing reading.[11] Of course, one of the most often quoted reasons for a haunting is that a spirit lingers to see an injustice put to rights. Indeed, as we shall see in the next chapter, just such an apparition has been seen — and heard — at Laura's graveside.

Laura's ghost was seen occasionally in the grounds of Oldstone Mansion, as reported in the early 1980s by dedicated Devonshire folklorist Theo Brown.[12] In 2005, Pat Bendall of Woodlands Leisure Park told me that her ghost is still said to haunt the woodland with the ponds where she loved to stroll and play with her dog. Pat did add, however, that she didn't know of any sightings herself, but she mentioned that the ruins themselves are also reputedly haunted.

The 'Ghost Room' with intact window frames is on the top floor.

Also in 2005 Dr Richard Porter told me that driving past Oldstone one morning, probably in October 1989, he noticed a man in black and a woman in white standing some thirty-five yards (32m) to the right of the ruin. He thought they must have been a bride and groom, and chanced to mention them to a friend who promptly claimed them to be the ghosts of Laura and her husband; and only then did he hear of the great mystery. If this was a haunting of the 'shade' variety, where actual events are faithfully

---

[11] Carole Thompson 1986, *The Blackawton Mystery*, Totnes, Totnes Community Archive.

[12] Theo Brown 1982, *Devon Ghosts*, 24, Norwich, Jarrold.

portrayed, it could offer a clue to the sequence of events that led up to the tragedy. Such hauntings are alleged to remain energised until the mystery is cleared up, at which point the psychic tension is released and the manifestations cease.

Ursula Dimes, the great, great granddaughter of William Dimes (Laura's grandfather) who bought Oldstone in 1839, wrote a section about ghosts in her book Oldstone,[13] and she very kindly gave me a collection of newspaper clippings that contain many of the tales.

The earliest of these newspaper articles,[14] in 1963, records how a room became known as the 'Ghost Room' after some of the family's younger children played a simple prank on an unsuspecting chimney sweep. It is unlikely that these children were Laura or her siblings, who were all born at Oldstone, as her father was a strict disciplinarian and such childish nonsense as a practical joke would have seemed severely out of place; instead, I favour the perpetrators as being among the many children of William Stephen Dimes, most of whom had been born in the London area, and would have relished the opportunities for mischief afforded by a great house such as Oldstone; indeed, some of them may have felt starved of excitement by having come to live in the countryside in about 1891.

HISTORY of psychic turbulence

Probably then, in or around 1892 the chimney sweep was working in a room on the second floor, when the impish youngsters locked the door, trapping him there. It seems an innocuous enough trick to play, but before long he was heard screaming to be set free. He explained, once he'd recovered wits enough, that he had seen visions of a battle so appalling in its carnage that he became desperate to escape.

This simple story loops back on itself in a remarkable way because by 1895 Oldstone Mansion had suffered a chimney fire (not connected with the chimney serving the Ghost Room) that quickly spread to engulf the entire building, reducing it to an empty shell.[15] The Ghost Room was the only room in the building that somehow retained intact the glass in its windows. A photograph taken some years later still showed this curious state, and thankfully Ursula made a faithful drawing of it, which is reproduced here — 'thankfully' because the original is now almost certainly lost.

The same paper mentions that the drive from the lodge to the mansion passes over a bridge built in 1842 above a farm road, and that a phantom figure walks beneath its arch at noon and midnight.

---

[13] Ursula Dimes 1985, *Oldstone*, Dartmouth, Carmina Publishing. Incidentally, I was proprietor of the small press that produced the book (a facsimile of Ursula's handwritten, personally illustrated volume) as a limited edition of 100 numbered copies. A typeset and edited edition was published under the same title in 1993 by the Dartmouth History Research Group.

[14] *The Western Morning News*, 3 May 1963.

[15] In 1976 the ruin of Oldstone House was protected when it became a Grade II listed building.

The newspaper publicity sparked further interest, and the following week a journalist whose identity is recorded in the byline simply as Westcountryman, reported meeting with Dorothy Sims (Ursula's grandfather's stepdaughter) of Torquay.[16] She told him she saw a ghost in the ruined mansion late one night around 1917. She was fifteen or sixteen years old and had been enjoying an alfresco supper along with a brother and some step-brothers and sisters, watching badgers in Oldstone's woods (it was a popular location for nature study groups in the years before the First World War). Her gaze had settled on the crumbling building and she noticed a woman leaning out of one of the mansion's ruined windows, her ghostly figure bathed in light. We may only speculate whether this light was from the disastrous fire.

The same article records that some un-named people from Blackawton had seen the ghosts of a man and woman alighting from a coach and entering the front door at midnight. This repeating haunting was particularly odd in that the coach that brings them along the drive to the house was drawn by headless horses.

In 1966 a journalist reported a ghostly carriage pulled by four horses driven at a gallop by a headless coachman — they careered along the drive, over the bridge, and right into and through the ruins of the great hall.[17] This article also mentions the ghost of a bearded old sailor who had lived in the hermitage in the grounds. This hermitage is a stone cell some four feet square (1.2m), and is situated in the woods not far from the lower of the three ponds, the uppermost of which claimed the life of Laura Dimes.

The article also mentions seemingly inexplicable sounds echoing around the ruin — the noise of wood being chopped (the journalist suggests a woodpecker as a natural explanation, but anyone familiar with the countryside would realise there is a huge difference between the rattling woodpecker and the slow methodical chop, chop, chop of the woodcutter's axe). Tradition maintained that these were actually related to the family that owned the building before the Dimes: the Cholwich family.

Once powerful merchants, the Cholwich family's dynastic aspirations ended in disaster when the last male heir was imprisoned for debt. Nevertheless, the family seem to have been highly regarded in the area; when the Dimes family took over as absentee landlords, upset villagers created an effigy of their new neighbour, paraded it through the streets and drowned it in a village pond. Despite its eerie resonance with the unexplained death of Laura in Oldstone's largest pond, it is surely too far-fetched to seriously contemplate a direct link (like a voodoo effigy) between the villagers' spontaneous demonstration of ire at William Dimes and the death of his granddaughter nearly fifty years later.

So far we have only considered ghosts that don't interact with the living, but now we must turn our attention to the spirits of people who, for one reason or another didn't move on when they passed away, and are still unmistakably alive. Although the difference between these types of haunting seems immense, the story of Laura Dimes bridges this divide.

---

[16] *The Western Morning News*, 17 May 1963.
[17] *Dartmouth Chronicle*, 20 May 1966.

CHAPTER TWO

THE LIVING DEAD

HE GHOSTS THAT ARE MOST FREQUENTLY REPORTED ARE OF THE SHADE VARIETY, AND ARE COMPLETELY OBLIVIOUS TO US; BUT THE GHOSTS WE'LL MEET IN THIS CHAPTER ARE FAR MORE EXCITING BECAUSE THEY ALL EXHIBIT THE DESIRE — AND ABILITY — TO COMMUNICATE WITH WITNESSES.

This sort of spirit is the star of innumerable Hollywood ghost stories in which it usually manifests in one of two stereotypical forms: either as a demonic poltergeist that terrorises everybody until its living victims defeat it in a spiritual battle; or as a pathetic soul cursed with a secret, roaming forever in a lonely earthbound existence until someone brave and compassionate enough releases it from its doom.

While both extremes are represented below, most hauntings by these lively spirits occupy the middle ground, and exhibit only mild or intermittent attempts to communicate with us. Sometimes, we may not even realise at the time that we are indeed in conversation with a ghost.

TALKING WITH STRANGERS

A ghost apparently seeking justice has been both seen and heard at the sombre Longcross Cemetery, Townstal (entrance in Townstal Road). A man in what seemed to be 19th century clothing appeared next to a bench on which Terry Pritchard was sitting, and the spectre struck up a conversation: "He got away with murder, you know."
"Who?" Terry replied.
"That one, over there."

Longcross Cemetery, Townstal (see pages 32,33,37,38 and rear endpapers).

Terry looked and, turning back to his companion, found he had vanished. Terry arose and followed the direction indicated, and found the gravestone of Laura Shortland (nee Dimes). At that time though, Terry hadn't heard of Laura, and it was only afterwards that his wife read the story of her death at Oldstone Mansion, Blackawton (a local TV channel also later featured the mystery), and identified her.

Possibly, the ghost was a relative or close friend of Laura, and was urging a forensic re-examination of the events that led to her death. In which case, maybe he was attempting to remove once and forever the stain of the possibility that she took her own life — a sin in the eyes of many. Or perhaps his motive was simply retribution against her assailant. But a more radical interpretation suggests that the ghost was that of her husband Hugh Shortland, who had been suspected of her murder in 1884. Following his acquittal he launched a vociferous campaign to find her murderer. But if — and it's a big IF because current opinion appears unanimous in suspecting him (although, it must be said, at the time of the trial the public sympathy in the Kingsbridge court was for and not against him) so — *if* Hugh Shortland was utterly blameless in his wife's death, then perhaps it was the bond of love that inspired him to remain holding a lonely vigil at his wife's grave, still seeking justice for her.

NEW LIGHT ON THE OLDSTONE MYSTERY

I returned to Blackawton and Oldstone in the autumn of 2005, having last seen it some twenty years previously, and stayed at Woodside Cottage as the guest of Sally and Tim Adams. Their cottage is 18th century in date and was the gamekeeper's lodge for the Oldstone estate, and I am happy to say it has been sensitively converted to provide luxury bed and breakfast accommodation in a wonderfully tranquil rural setting.

We discussed the local legends about Oldstone, and Sally enquired whether I might bring a psychic medium along to sort out the cause of Laura Shortland's death, once and for all. It is often from such a chance comment, that important developments spring, and her gentle nudge sparked off a strange little adventure.

The idea hinged on whether the ghostly figure of Laura was a shade, mindlessly re-enacting certain key moments in her life, or sentient and willing and able to communicate with us. I knew of the Torbay Investigators of the Paranormal (TIP is well-known in the Torbay area, and holds weekly meetings whose attendance would be the envy of many a small organisation's annual get-together), and had heard their team included a practised medium — would they be interested in trying to solve the mystery of Laura's demise?

Whatever your beliefs about the possibility of contacting the spirits of the dead, there is no denying that many mediums train themselves to become exceptionally sensitive to ideas and influences that most people would overlook or ignore. In this way, a competent medium may intuitively perceive links between data where no logical connection exists, and be able to offer unique insights into a situation. In short, they may find clues where others have failed. With this in mind, I knew the answer to the famous ghostbusting question 'who you gonna call?' I called TIP.

David Phillips, TIP chairman, promptly arranged for Maia, the team's "medium of choice" to visit the site. We — David, Maia, fellow TIP team member Richard Potter, and myself — arrived at Woodside Cottage at 5:30pm on Wednesday September 28th, in a mini convoy of three cars. I had to congratulate David on keeping unbroken TIP's record of its trips always enjoying good weather, for the heavy rain of the afternoon had just spluttered to a halt and blue sky was shining through the breaking clouds above us.

Having briefly introduced ourselves to Sally and Tim, who had arranged with Pat Bendall of Woodlands Leisure Park for her kind permission to visit the valley ponds, we set off into the woods around 5:45pm with Tim in the lead. The scramble through steep woodland, slippery with the first fallen leaves of the season, was treacherous and slowed our progress. We also paused periodically whenever Maia wished to focus on sensitising herself to the location (we had withheld information from her about the haunting). The distraction of keeping a sure footing as we went deeper into the darkening woodland, made this a very difficult assignment for any medium, but Maia loves woods and valiantly persevered, and I was fortunate enough to capture her comments on a digital recorder.

At one point half way up the side of the hill to the west of the valley, Maia 'picked up' or became aware of the spirits of two young girls, aged seven or eight, who were sisters, possibly twins. She said "These girls were involved in the planting of this bit of woodland." Then the girls showed her how the landscape as it was before the wood grew. "What they're sharing with me is there's more daylight — [it's] more open — and they're planting the trees around them."

In the same area Maia also picked up on a sort of procession or dance consisting solely of men (the women and children were onlookers). She felt that it would have been part of a ceremonial occasion, possibly a formal one such as beating the bounds. Although this echo of ancient ritual activity intrigued us, the heavy rain had suddenly started again, and the clouds made the growing darkness more intense. We had to push forward towards the site of Laura's death.

Despite this growing sense of urgency, as we approached the valley, Maia paused once more to concentrate on another presence. "There's a single male entity. He's fair-haired, quite young, and a very lost soul — he's not doing any harm, but I think people have seen him. He's just wandering around — looking for something he's lost, and in the process of doing that he's approaching the living and spooking them.

"What is he searching for? It's something he buried here. It was important to him, and he can't remember where he left it. I'm seeing the original box, it's a bit coffin-like, and there are some paper items in there, like maps. There are also some old brass instruments, like telescopes. They were in the family but the house where they were came under attack or something, and he needed to move them to a place of safety. But now he can't find them.

"I'll try and pin it down a bit more — what the source of the trouble was... I'm seeing the old Customs and Excise. He ran up here to hide it, and buried it, and forgot where he put it!

"I want to ask him if there is any reason why he can't leave it now... Wow, I wasn't expecting this answer. He was saying it's meaningful to somebody in the living now. So there's somebody alive, who knew he'd done this, and he's trying to find it so he can tell them."

between two worlds

His story of buried treasures and maps or possibly nautical charts showing the location of who-knows-what, was difficult to ignore but we were pressed for time. In fact, Tim had to return home to keep a prior engagement, so we lost our guide through the woods. The worsening weather and early nightfall meant we were unable to spend any quality time at the pond in which Laura's body had been found. However, when we arrived back in the village, we debriefed in the congenial setting of at the George Inn, and Maia made some more interesting observations.

"As we left the area, I had a very strong feeling that the subject was a woman. It was like she was reaching out to me from the pond area where I felt a column of light, which I felt was a very nice area [the lower of the ponds]. And what she showed me was like a willow-pattern arch bridge, [she was] standing in the middle, leaning, looking down — and she was agonisingly contemplating something. She said 'The bridge isn't actually here, I'm just showing you the bridge.' Now, whether she meant the bridge is no longer there, or it's a metaphor, I'm not sure. I don't usually do metaphors — they [the spirits] usually show me what's actually happening."

A little later, convinced now that the woman (who she described as quite young and pretty, with longish hair) had drowned, Maia took up the story again. "It's like she's slowly going down, and she's holding something. It's not like she's doing it deliberately, but she's not struggling at all."

Maia sought to discover what the young woman was holding as she sank under the surface of the pond, and said "I'm getting very strange Christian images — like she's thinking about a big cross, like a stone cross, almost Celtic — ancient — stone. I just felt very strong Christian beliefs, and there's a feeling like 'There's no way out.' It's like she's boxed in with her thoughts, and she doesn't think that whatever is making her grieve is forgivable. It's like no-one's going to forgive her — I don't believe that's true, but she felt that."

Even under optimum conditions, Maia would start to feel the strain of communicating with the spirit world after about an hour, but the long walk through the storm-soaked woods had tired us all (I certainly couldn't think straight, and am grateful I had the technology to record the conversation). It's no wonder that, after three hours, Maia was becoming increasingly hesitant over how to interpret what she was picking up. It wasn't until she'd had a good sleep that she realised the image of the old stone cross was probably another metaphor — Oldstone Cross — which is on the main Dartmouth-Totnes road at the junction with the country lane that runs past Oldstone Manor from Blackawton. Many people visiting the Manor would have used the Oldstone Cross turning.

However, Maia persevered, and the impromptu session in the pub continued, and she made a number of interesting comments that I have edited together to give an impression of the young woman's final moments: "She's accepting this, like the enveloping of Mother Earth — finally loving her... I felt she was killed by the pressure of other people... The bit that's pulling her down is the weight of the guilt... She could have fought it, she could easily have got up and walked away... I'm feeling really angry on her behalf... She was a lovely girl."

The subject of the bridge cropped up again because Maia now saw the young woman standing on flat stones. David, who had remained remarkably level headed and on-the-ball, suggested that "The way you say 'bridge, but it's not a bridge' — it's like a crossover, like in her mind she's in a state between two worlds."

Maia agreed "It's very much like that kind of thing. The willow pattern — the mythical bridge — yeah."

So the bridge could be another metaphor describing the spirit's condition, but the reference to the willow pattern may also be relevant. This famous design, Chinese in flavour and first used on English ceramics in the late 18th century, illustrates a tragic story of young love. The young couple are eloping and are pursued across the bridge by the maiden's enraged father (although they escape overseas, he eventually finds them and they perish — their spirits becoming the two birds at the top of the design).[1]

Maia also tried to pick up on her name but admitted "I'm not very good on names." She felt the first name had two syllables, something like Sarah, and she said she 'saw' the surname as a "short, three letters name." This may seem a long way from Laura Shortland, but there's not so very much difference between Laura and Sarah, and the big clue to the surname was how short it was — *Short*land?

The last impressions Maia received were "I'm not quite sure what she was holding... but she was definitely holding grief." And concluded with a poignant indication of how the young woman had been feeling. In the woman's own words: "I can't bear it any more — my heart's broken — I'm giving up."

---

[1] The story is likely to be an English creation rather than an original Chinese fable.

It must be noted that the pond Maia referred to was not the uppermost one where Laura's body was found, but the lowest. However, the upper reaches of this wooded valley have been developed into the Woodlands Leisure Park, a popular tourist attraction occupying a 60 acre (24 ha) site that offers a wide variety of rides and activities for children, which means that the tranquillity of the woodland ponds Laura loved so dearly is now most strongly felt around the lower pond.

This TIP investigation did not solve the key issue of whether newlywed Laura Shortland's death was a result of accident, suicide or foul play; indeed, it probably raises more questions than it answers. But, in a way, I am pleased this mystery remains for others to ponder and, one day perhaps, solve.

vengeance of a woman wronged

A much less tranquil tale of the ghost of a wronged woman is set in the Mansion House in Mansion House Street, Dartmouth, which is regarded as the finest Georgian building in the town although a casual glance at the exterior reveals little of note. The Mansion House was built around 1730 and was used frequently in the 18th century for civic functions involving the Lord Mayor and other dignitaries, and was sometimes even the scene of lavish entertainment and carousing of an allegedly decadent variety. The main room on the first floor has exuberant panels with Bacchic figures and other classical deities of suitably light-hearted bearing; and it was said that anyone who dared leave a revel early had to suffer payment of a forfeit.

But not all was fun and games. The legend relates how one resident's amorous indiscretion brought a curse upon the house. A maidservant became pregnant, but her plea for maintenance was refused. In fact, the embarrassed man threw her out of her job and out of his life. Or so he hoped.

The distraught woman returned to her family home but found no refuge there either. Her future must have appeared fraught with impossible difficulties and, tragically, clutching her babe to her breast, she walked down into the cold, swirling waters of the Dart's smothering embrace.

On the stroke of midnight, the soul of this drowned mother returned to the Mansion with the ghost of her child in her arms. They entered through the front door, a privilege that would never have been given her as a servant, but should have been the birthright of her child, and slowly ascended the stairs whose ceiling depicts the astrological signs of the zodiac, seeking out that upper chamber where the disastrous injustice had occurred.

This routine was repeated at midnight with appalling regularity, and a local newspaper[2] reported that the family living in the Mansion House in the 1940s were

---

[2] *Herald Express*, 11 November 1959.

being badly disturbed by the ghosts. In the family it seemed the daughters and their mother were particularly affected, and the head of the household, Mr G H Lane, an antiques dealer, went so far as to install a mantrap on the stairs.

The building's owners in the early 1980s experienced nothing supernatural, and although subsequent owner Mrs Miles witnessed an apparition in the middle of the 1980s, this spirit had a gentle disposition. She told me her ghost was that of a maid in a white mob-cap and a full skirt of pale blue, carefully cleaning one of the upstairs windows. Mrs Miles saw her clearly yet felt no anxiety whatsoever, indeed this manifestation seemed to reflect the tranquillity that had somehow returned to the building despite its reincarnation as a busy shop selling household goods. It is just possible that this maid was actually the same maidservant who had suffered so terribly, but Mrs Miles had seen her at an earlier time in her life, a moment perhaps when her prospects had looked bright, her spirits were high and she was at peace with the world.

In 1988 the shop was converted into a restaurant run by the Cranfield family and, although they fell in love with the building, they felt there was something a little unsettling about its atmosphere. Again the young daughter Hannah and her mother Helen seemed to suffer most. Hannah recently told me how they were often both disturbed by the sounds of a baby screaming at night, cries that could never be explained satisfactorily. Mercifully though, the midnight spectre that climbed the spiralling stairs did not reappear.

tHe ROMANtIC ɢHosts of ɢommeRock castLe

Another tale of romantic love is celebrated at Gommerock Castle, which boasts more than one story, the first of which contains something of an enigma. The castle has been a ruin since the late 17th century, and lies some 350 yards (320m) upstream of Kingswear Castle, shrouded in the woodland that lines the Dart from Kingswear to the sea. It was amid these ruins that a skeleton was unearthed in the first half of the 19th century. Details of this, our first story, are recounted in a small book by Arthur Holdsworth the last Governor of Dartmouth Castle.[3]

The surgeon who examined the remains considered the skull to be of a male type; unfortunately, he made no mention of the pelvis, which is much less ambiguous for the forensic determination of sex. At any rate, the labourer who discovered the grave was in no doubt that its occupant was female, and later offered the following justification: "There was a woman, more than a century ago, who used to frequent that Castle. She was often seen wandering about the adjoining cliffs, but suddenly disappeared: and I have no doubt that these bones must be the remains of that unfortunate creature."

---

[3] Arthur Holdsworth 1844, *Gomerock Castle or the Grave of the Unknown*, privately printed.

The person he was talking to was inclined to be sceptical, which prompted the labourer to retort: "You may smile, but I could name the persons who have seen a woman's form pass close before them here, in the night, and suddenly be lost. Strange things were spoken of before our master came to live here;[4] noises were heard, and Mountain's Gate has opened for the traveller without mortal hands."

This reference to Mountain's Gate baffles me. It could be a reference to a myth I'm unfamiliar with, or may be a quasi-religious euphemism for somebody disappearing as if the earth opened and swallowed them, but I am also reminded of the story retold in our final chapter, about the mountain caves in which the giants of Albion lived — could this phrase be a survival of that tradition, whose meaning was already lost?

Holdsworth goes on to tell the romantic story of the maiden Maria Blackaller of the Ferry Inn, Kingswear, who committed suicide by leaping from the cliffs below the ruin when she came to believe her lover, a sailor, had been slain by a rival. Tragically, she was mistaken, and it was only her own lack of faith that prevented their happy reunion.

Apart from the woman's ghost haunting the area, there was also apparently a male spirit that lurked in the ruins. His story, which is also linked to the skeleton, is told in *Ye Legende of Gomerocke*,[5] which tells in verse the tale of two young lovers who plighted their troth at the ruin of Gommerock Castle.

At one point, the spirit of the unknown man in the grave appears to the young man and tests his love for the maiden. The fearsome ordeal requires the youth to return in seven days time, at midnight, and face the ghost alone. The young lover accepts the challenge and, true to his word, keeps the appointment. When he arrives back at Gommerock Castle he sits upon a stone seat beneath a rock and awaits the spirit's appearance. The poet muses upon the chilling scene...

> *Those who in contemplation dwell*
> *On scenes long-loved and cherished well,*
> *Have often felt some secret power*
> *At midnight's deep and holy hour,*
> *When the soul seems to quit the clay,*
> *And soar in regions far away.*

This verse seems to describe the out-of-the-body experience, or astral projection. And the narrator adds that at such times we may also...

---

[4] Presumably Mr Holdsworth himself, who had acquired Gommerock in the 1820s.
[5] Arthur Holdsworth 1878, *Gomerock Castle or the Grave of the Unknown*, Dartmouth, Cranford. This posthumous edition of Holdsworth's book includes the long poem *Ye Legende of Gomerocke* by an author identified only by the initials U B E.

> *Summon forms that from earth have fled*
> *Hold converse with the silent dead,*
> *Review the cherish'd scenes of old*
> *That closely does the heart enfold.*

Both sorts of ghostly phenomena are mentioned there: the sentient spirit and the imprint of an historical scene. The ghost of the unknown man makes a similar point when he eventually arrives, and adds the ingredient that is otherwise so notably absent from this collection: the nocturnal visit from a close relative or friend —

> *And spirits now communion keep,*
> *Around some loved ones as they sleep;*

Finally, the "Unknown" as the ghost is called throughout, reports to the maiden (in song) that the youth, her lover, is true to her:

> *His heart is as true as the needle to thine*
> *That points to the North, whatever the range.*
> *His spirit's as pure as the bright star above,*
> *By which thou hast vowed to be faithful to him.*

And continues...

> *As the branch that he brake, as it clung to the tree,*
> *As the bonds of that ivy, he clings to thee.*[6]

This *Legende*, which is fascinating in its own right, also casts an interesting light upon my concluding remark about the giant Goemagot (discussed in our final chapter), inasmuch as this ghost, whose body lay at Gommerock, was a guardian spirit whose duty was to challenge those who ventured past, and determine whether they be friend or foe.

spectre of a spiteful father

Our next story takes a different slant from the Gommerock tale in which a ghost challenges the male half of a loving couple: here the ghost pits his wits against a woman in love. Forbidden love is the central theme for this antique story whose terrifying events could form the plot of a modern horror

---

[6] Ivy's habit of embracing its host, as well as its evergreen nature, made it a popular rustic metaphor for enduring love (it is not a parasitic plant as some people nowadays suppose). Its clinging habit is so strong that should its host tree die and completely decay, the ivy may continue to intertwine with itself and become a self-supporting structure — a truly independent ivy tree.

film.[7] The Mount Boone estate was located at the top of Ridge Hill, Dartmouth, in the fork between Mount Boone Lane and Mount Boone, and although the house was demolished in 1905, long stretches of its high garden wall survive (indeed, when I visited in the centenary of its destruction, I was greatly entertained by a bat flitting to and fro above the ancient castellated wall).

The story concerns Thomas Boone who was born around 1610 in Townstal, became the local Squire, and acquired the Mount Boone estate in 1635. He was in harmony with the townsfolk in his support for the Parliamentarian cause, and became Member of Parliament for Dartmouth. He became a personal friend of Oliver Cromwell and was despatched on diplomatic missions to Denmark and Sweden, and even to the Russian court. Clearly, Thomas Boone was a confident, capable and assertive man and a vigorous spirit that was difficult to defy.

Tradition tells that his daughter fell in love with a man Thomas deemed unsuitable. I dare say his daughter inherited much of Thomas' determination, but the patriarch eventually compelled her to renounce the call of her heart, and she took a solemn oath breaking off the engagement. But not long after this dreadful domestic upset, on Monday January 26th, 1679 (1680),[8] Thomas Boone passed away, and his daughter promptly renounced her vow. Before long, the happy couple were settling into the comforts of her ancestral home, Mount Boone.

I examined the genealogy of this family and found that Thomas' daughter Anne married in the year following his death, her groom was Francis Drake, baronet of Buckland. Francis was a nephew of Sir Francis Drake who, although knighted by Queen Elizabeth I, was regarded by many of his peers as little more than a pirate. Perhaps it was this family that Thomas Boone regarded with such mistrust.

However, the late Squire did not take matters lying down; indeed he prowled the house hell-bent on exacting vengeance for his daughter's disrespect to his memory. Each night he made his feelings clear by igniting spectral lights, uttering unearthly noises, and heaving heavy furniture about. His ghost was also seen increasingly often both in the house and grounds as he persecuted her relentlessly.

The constant nervous strain began to affect her health, and the couple took the advice of physicians and fled to London. But so tenacious was his wrath that he simply moved with them. They returned to Mount Boone, and the haunting carried on much as before except that Thomas appeared now in the day as well as at night.

---

[7] This traditional story was recounted in 1879, *Collectanea Curiosa Devoniensia*, Transactions of the Devonshire Association, 11, 344 - 345; by J Coxhead 1967, *The Devil in Devon*, Bracknell, West Country Handbooks; and by Ralph Whitlock 1977, *The Folklore of Devon*, London, Batsford.

[8] At that period, and during the preceding Tudor period, New Year's Day was officially March 25th, which meant January 1679 came *after* December 1679. I have adopted the modern convention regarding affected dates from 1 January to 24 March, by showing the year as they knew it, followed (in parentheses) by the year as we would reckon it.

Facing a harrowing winter that could cost the young wife's life, they called upon the local clergy to intervene. The resulting ritual of exorcism must have been accompanied by a tremendous outpouring of psychic fury from the ghost because the endeavour teetered on the brink of utter failure until, as all hope seemed lost, the late Thomas Boone appeared in the room and spoke to the horrified group. He offered to leave the house forever on condition that his daughter would accompany him to the grave.

trickster

The clergymen deliberated and declared that they were willing to accept his macabre contract, but insisted on adjourning to the banks of the nearby stream at Castle Mill (presumably located by the Hermitage Castle, Old Mill Creek). Having lured the ghost to the water's edge, the clergy renewed their efforts with bell, book and candle, and played a fateful gambit by announcing that Thomas must first empty all the water from the stream using only a cockle shell.

Thomas was nobody's fool yet he agreed to the new constraint, and the minister declared that he just happened to have a cockle shell on him, which he promptly produced — it had a large hole in it. But even so the ferocious ghost remained compliant, and accepted the shell from the wily cleric. His daughter asked if he were content with the arrangement, to which he replied with a doom-laden growl "You will see."

With that the assembly dispersed, and the couple went back to the house feeling profoundly relieved, confident that the late Squire's task would keep him busy until Doomsday. They enjoyed a peaceful life together for the first time ever, but they did not have long to celebrate their victory — Thomas Boone's daughter died before thirteen weeks passed. Is it possible that the cunning Squire found a loophole to beat the ruse of the leaky shell?

In 1681 a memorial of black and white marble was erected in honour of Thomas Boone in the church of St Clement at Townstal, and a wooden board at St Petrox commemorates his gift "to ye Poare of this town £10 pr Annvm to be for ever Payd by his heirs". Despite this act of charity, it is said the ghost of Thomas Boone remained ill at ease for many a year afterwards and continued to haunt his ancestral home. The clattering of hooves as he rode through the courtyard was often heard (indeed, in the 1980s local residents said he is still occasionally seen, both on horseback and on foot),[9] and people swore that he could sometimes be heard weaving ropes of sand for his master, the Devil. A more kindly epitaph, and of which he most likely would have approved, was given by a contemporary who knew him well; the gist of which runs — although he only had one eye, he saw more clearly than most men with two.[10]

---

[9] Peter Underwood 1982, *Ghosts of Devon*, Bodmin, Bossiney Books.
[10] Percy Russell 1950, *Dartmouth*, London, Batsford.

Perhaps the following tale told to me by Darren Clarke, of a ghost in the Old Mill area who repeatedly calls out "More rope!" is also a relic of the Thomas Boone story. The version Darren heard explained the haunting in terms of somebody who drowned because a line that might have saved him wasn't long enough for him to reach. But I wonder if it might be the cry of a doomed soul working out his penance — endlessly striving to make more rope of sand.

Another local tale set alongside Old Mill Creek involves a teenage woman who drowned in a well there, her cries for help echoing through the years. My thanks to Anna Sewell who shared that tale with me, and also for the snippet of information that music from the early 1800s has been heard in the vicinity of an old folly at Old Mill — music with no apparent natural source.

not poltergeists — *peskygeists*!

There are many other local reports of ghosts moving physical objects around at will, but these spirits utterly lack the malevolence of the Mount Boone haunting, and instead seem content to simply attract attention by performing astonishing tricks.

The Royal Castle Hotel, Dartmouth, offers us several such stories. Our first is set in The Galleon Bar (a long bar on the right hand side of the building as seen from the front), the rear of which was once a separate, quiet room mostly used by residents, and was known simply as the 'back bar'. Ron Green (also known as 'Big Ron') was born Dartmouth in the 1950s and is still well known locally for his dedication to charity work, and told me of an experience he had there. He emphasised that even though he was in the bar he was teetotal.

Early one evening in the late summer in 1965 or 1966, he was sitting in the back bar opposite the old fireplace, and was waiting to be joined by some friends who were staying at the hotel. He had not yet bought a drink (which would anyway have been non-alcoholic) when his attention was caught by an empty tumbler on a table next to him: "It came up off the table — about a foot — as if a person had picked it up and had it in their hand, and put it down on the next table, about a foot and a half away. I sat there and watched it, dazed."

The simplicity of this account is striking: had somebody wished to invent such a story they would doubtlessly have embellished it with mid air somersaults and could easily have rounded it off with a dramatic smash at their feet.

Although they may be unrelated as they lack psychokinetic elements, it is notable that the back bar is the scene of several other supernatural sightings. In 1985 a guest saw a ghostly huntsman materialise in front of the fireplace in the same back bar; and a night porter also frequently saw a youngish man walk through the stone wall at the rear end of the Galleon Bar, and move around near the fireplace there. The same night porter also saw and heard the ghosts of two men fighting. Nigel Way, owner of the hotel, told me "They passed straight through a modern partition wall near the main entrance, and continued to the back of the [Galleon] bar. The witness claimed that he discovered he had spots of rain on him, which indicates that the fight took place before the courtyard was covered in 1812." Nigel added "I'm not a ghostly person, but I have a funny feeling that most probably in that little back corner all the way up through the [back of the] building there is something."

In 1979 Lesley Park, a newspaper reporter, spent an eventful night in the reputedly haunted Room 6, on the first floor.[11] She held vigil until around 2:30am but was deprived of sleep by a mysterious thudding sound that continued on and off for about two hours. At 4:30am she was rendered wide awake by the sensation of being shaken. Feeling cold all over yet determined to investigate the phenomenon, she leaped out of bed, but there was nobody in her room.

Even if sleep had been possible after such a supernatural fright, she was denied it by her usually trustworthy alarm clock, which malfunctioned three times, startling her out of her doze. And when she finally arose to dress, she discovered her bra had been moved from where she had left it, and she eventually found it on the other side of the room in front of the so-called Priest's Hole.

The strange booming reminds me of something I experienced when I stayed in Room 22 (on the top, third floor) on the evening of Monday September 26th, 2005. I noticed it several times, and each time I was disturbed to find it was more of a visceral sensation than a sound —I felt it through my body rather than hearing it with my ears. This was certainly on the outer fringe of commonplace experience, and more than anything else seemed reminiscent of how a mother's pounding heartbeat might be experienced by a babe in the womb. Happily, I managed to identify its source: it was simply the reverberating footsteps of staff and guests along a particular stretch of the hallways. As it was neither protracted nor too intrusive, I relaxed and felt completely at ease in the room, and enjoyed an undisturbed night.

It is likely that the Priest's Hole has a mundane explanation too. Rather than being a hiding-place for persecuted Catholics (Dartmouth inclined towards Protestantism), it is probably an architectural void, a by-product of the conversion of the room. Most old houses have such spaces, which are periodically created and destroyed as fashions and changing needs remodel the rooms. The recent insertion of a small cross into the hole will doubtlessly tend to magnify the idea of it having supernatural significance.

---

[11] *Dartmouth Chronicle*, 30 November 1979, and Deryck Seymour 1990, *The Ghosts of Torbay*, Exeter, Obelisk Publications.

Room 22 has also witnessed the ghostly disarranging of guest's clothes, which have been reportedly found strewn on the floor, having first been removed from the chest of drawers.[12]

Another of the hotel's more bizarre traditions is that a couple of homosexual monks haunted one of the best rooms in the hotel. Their presence was not, apparently, confined to simple appearances but extended to the rather odd practice of turning paintings around on their hangings. Also, if the staff moved any furniture, it would be found the next morning back in its original position. The pair's antics are said to have kept the room locked and out of use for years, but all seems quiet nowadays.

Another incident involving the rearrangement of domestic furnishings occurred at Agincourt House. For many years until the mid 1990s it was an antiques shop and during that period there were reports of furniture such as chairs moving around on the first floor while there was nobody around. Perhaps those incidents were connected with the antiques themselves rather than Agincourt House.

There have also been reports of phenomena resembling that of a minor poltergeist at The Spinning Wheel Tea Rooms, but not in recent years. For instance, a tall-backed, three-seater bench was seen rocking to and fro all by itself, and the rattling of cutlery has brought staff into deserted rooms to find tabletops that had been carefully laid were now in complete disarray. And once a black plastic bowl was spirited out of a closed cabinet, and left sitting in the middle of the floor.

The Seven Stars, Smith Street, Dartmouth, has enjoyed a reputation for its ghosts for many a year. Anthony Hemmings used to work in and live at the pub, and in the evening, after it was closed, he told me he "used to hear footsteps in the restaurant above, that were going into the kitchen. The building is old so it does creak a bit, but you could definitely hear footsteps."

However, manifestations seem to be continuing on the first floor as current landlord Mike Priest told me that the cups hooked onto wooden beams in the restaurant's ceiling have a habit of jumping off their hooks when nobody is there, and smashing on the floor. This is where the ghost of an old lady in a green dress was seen in around 2001, but there may be no connection between her and the poltergeist activities.

In the 1980s I heard that a barman saw a ghostly woman in the cellar standing beneath the barrel ramp; uniquely this sighting was accompanied by scrabbling noises like radio static. Another old lady was seen in July 2005 by a woman staying in one of the first floor guest rooms. The visitor spent a pleasant hour sitting beside the fireplace talking with the ghostly old lady, who had long grey hair, wore a black dress and shawl and claimed to have lived in the building for 200 years.

---

[12] John & Anne Spencer 2000, *Collins Ghost Hunter's Guide to Britain*, London, Collins.

Not long afterwards, David Bell, a local decorator, was working in the hall outside the same room. He told me that around lunch time he was papering the walls and heard footsteps in that room, which he knew to be unoccupied. The sounds approached the door and the handle turned with a creaking squeak — but nobody was there. These incidents all seem to be merely pranks intended to amaze rather than upset anyone, japes of a playful nature from someone simply looking for a little attention.

Another ghost noted for fiddling with door handles was at The Cherub, Higher Street, where a man was rumoured to haunt a room on the second floor — which is all well and good, except that the room in question was used as the ladies' lavatory at the time. Fortunately, he was perfectly innocuous, and not in the least bit worrying except in the sense that the presence of a ghost who can turn door handles tended to be somewhat unsettling. Reported by at least three women (firstly in 1967, and the others in the early 1980s) he was perfectly genial in manner, early middle aged, and had a friendly, chubby face (almost cherubic in fact).

Another odd occurrence at The Cherub happened in November or December around 2003 when Chloe, a barmaid, saw a spirits tumbler on a shelf above the bar drop *diagonally* and smash a Bells whisky optic.

PUBS, MONKS AND POLTERGEISTS

A pub in Blackawton, The George Inn, has a long history of weird events. This rural pub was rebuilt in the early years of the 20th century after a disastrous fire, but a building on this site was the home of craftsmen working on the adjacent church of St Michael in the 15th century. The shadowy figure of a hooded man has been seen here, on and off for about fifty years, and is usually referred to as 'the monk'.

Kathie Langford was among the first in living memory to see him. She worked behind the bar in the 1960s, and told me she never saw him when she was alone, but always in the company of Bill the landlord. She never felt frightened by him, and he appeared so often, both during the day and at night, that Bill gave him the nickname "Fred".

On one occasion she was playing dominoes with Bill in the lounge, and a customer was drinking at the bar, when all three of them noticed somebody cross the room — but there was nobody there. The man at the bar was startled and asked "Did you see that?"

Bill made a joke of it to soothe the stranger's nerves, saying "Oh you've just seen the monk, Fred."

Unfortunately Kathie never got a good look at the monk, who only ever appeared as a fleeting shadow or glimpsed out of the corner of an eye.

She told me that around the same time Bill Davis, a local coalman, saw a ghostly hooded figure dressed in black walking up the road in front of him, outside the inn. Talk in the village died down a bit after the local vicar claimed that his wife had seen the monk one day in church.

In the summer of 1992 Richard and Sally Tomlinson took over the pub, and in September they noticed the sound of heavy footsteps from the passageway above the bar, but when they went up to the first floor to investigate, there was no sign of the cause. Patrons of the pub heard it too, and noted that the steps always walked in the same direction. Mr Tomlinson was initially sceptical about ghosts but, having noted their invisible regular seemed friendly enough, was inclined to leave him be.

When contacting a local newspaper Mr Tomlinson also mentioned the story of the hooded figure, and added that two small children had been seen in a guest's bedroom — but just their outlines.[13]

Vic Hall took over the George in 2002 and although he didn't notice anything out of the ordinary himself, he did tell me he'd heard the pub was haunted by the ghost of "a young lass" and sometimes lights that had been turned off at night were found switched on again in the morning.

Graham Bennett took over at the start of August 2005, and within the month he had an extraordinary experience. One morning he awoke to find the first floor office door open (it had been securely locked the night before), and its locked filing cabinet had a drawer pulled wide open. Nothing had been taken, and there were no signs of an intruder; and the only set of keys was still secure where he'd left them the previous evening.

Around 10am he went downstairs and soon started hearing bangs from the first floor — doors were slamming, repeatedly. He went up to find out what was going on (there were no residents in the guest rooms) and "found all the carpets rumpled up and folded into corners."

Since then there haven't been any more major incidents, just a stream of ongoing minor poltergeist activity ranging from heavy sash windows opening and shutting on their own, to lights turning themselves on overnight; and the sound of footsteps in the upstairs rooms and hall are frequently heard when nobody is up there. Doors often open and close by themselves, and on one memorable occasion Graham was sitting with a couple of other people in the bar late one evening when they saw the latch rise on the door to the side room (which gives access to the stairs); the door swung open but no one was there. Then the door closed and latched itself shut again.

Life is also made difficult by lots of small items such as keys, phones, and shopping

---

[13] *Dartmouth Chronicle*, 30 October 1992.

lists inexplicably going missing, only to turn up in unexpected places. Graham noted that, frustratingly, these events seem to happen just at the most inconvenient moments. Fortunately though, Graham is able to take all this in his stride.

Another pub, the Tower Inn, Church Road, Slapton, has long been the focus for paranormal phenomena. It dates from the 14th century when it was a row of six cottages and, like the George Inn, originally provided accommodation for the craftsmen building the adjacent ecclesiastical establishments. The charming inn is visually dominated by an imposing 80-foot (24m) tower that is the sole substantial relic of a college and chantry founded in 1372. Given this exceptional association, I find it surprising monks don't figure more prominently in the many reports from this inn. The first potentially monkish report I found is of a ghostly figure dressed in 'Middle Ages' clothes seen in the room on the far right of the main entrance.

I was fortunate enough to spend a happy hour or two in that very room in the very congenial company of local astrologer Felicity, Janette Khan (whose daughter and son-in-law ran the inn in the 1980s and 1990s), and David Phillips who had kindly volunteered to chauffeur me around some of his favourite haunts in the South Hams. And they had plenty of tales to tell.

tales from the tower

The landlord in 2006 told me he had nothing odd to report from the couple of years he has been there, but the staff mentioned people would sometimes feel they were tapped on the shoulder when there was nobody else around. Janette enlarged upon this, saying that over the years many people had felt that ghostly hand on their shoulders, particularly in the cellar behind the bar, which was built in the mid 1980s. Rumour I heard later hinted that this hand belongs to a figure swathed in a cloak — or a monk in a habit.

Felicity told me that after that bout of structural alterations, which included moving the bar from the left hand side of the inn to its present location to the right of the entrance, the eerie sound of a baby crying upstairs was first noticed. It was around this time too that she saw a shadowy figure she described as a Cavalier coming rushing down the stairs as fast as if he was on horseback, and out through the front door. She added that a friend saw the same thing around that time. This friend, incidentally, lived in Slapton and her house suffered some slight poltergeist activity involving ornaments being moved around rooms, and taps being turned fully on when nobody was about. Felicity remembered a spate of poltergeist activity around that time at the Tower itself, including displacements of various decorations in the rooms, and Janette particularly recalled a string of bells that used to hang there, which started jingling all on its own.

Janette said it was about the same period that landlords heard a lot of commotion after they had closed up for the night; it seemed as if there was a party going on downstairs, but nobody was there. Felicity recalled an old tale she'd heard about a wedding reception held there, during which a particular photograph of the wedding party had been taken outside in what is now a parking area. The picture chanced to show the image of an old man gazing down from a window above the main door — the odd thing being that he had died some time previously. Perhaps coincidentally, an old man has been seen on several occasions sitting by the old fireplace.

There was a well outside the kitchen windows in the beer garden at the back of the inn, and Felicity told me that in or around 1987 a young teenage girl around 15 years old, was frequently seen peering in through that kitchen window. She wore long clothes that seemed appropriate to the 18th century, and appeared at different times of the day.

Janette said that a dark apparition of a cloaked figure wearing a large hat had been seen in 1988 in the room above the inn's kitchen. And she added that around 1990 a couple of lodgers were horrified when they saw a ghost appear through the wall, and stoop over their bed holding what appeared to be a knife. The man challenged the ghostly intruder, who promptly vanished. David mentioned that a few years ago he had spoken to the landlords, and learned that the landlady's mother had stayed in the room above the kitchen: she heard very heavy footsteps coming up to her door, which opened, but nobody entered. This disturbance had happened on more than one occasion. David also said that staff reported that the kitchen's saloon doors had a tendency to swing open on their own.

Felicity, who moved to the village more than twenty years ago and feels Slapton is her spiritual home, told me that one evening after leaving the inn she was surprised to discover she was being escorted by five ghostly monks along the road that leads northwest. They walked to either side and behind her in a protective formation and offered her a clear and comforting message that "It's going to be alright."

Mrs Jane Ashby of Start House, told me of a woman staying at a cottage in Slapton, who saw the figure of a ghostly monk standing in her garden. So, although not particularly prominent at the inn itself, it seems that past inhabitants of the chantry college may yet remain to cast their spiritual influence over the area.

stormy George

The *Edgcumbe Belle*, formerly known as the *Humphrey Gilbert*, was launched in 1957: the vessel is some 60 feet (nearly 20m) in length, and was commissioned by British Rail to provide a passenger ferry service for railway passengers between the station and hotel at Kingswear and the terminus at Dartmouth (where it had a ticket office, now the Station Restaurant, South Embankment). It is said to be haunted by a ghost that James Thomas calls 'George'.

James told me "He only turns up when the weather is stormy and blowing a gale. I've seen him twice. The first was in the winter of 1997." James was a deckhand at the time, and the boat was moored at the Dartmouth pontoon. "At about 7:30pm I was walking down the ramp, and saw a gentleman sat just inside the saloon deck (the covered area) on the port side. He was wearing waterproofs — a black sou'wester, and black oilskins. His collar was turned up, and his sou'wester pulled down, so it was hard to see his face, only his nose — which was big and bulbous like an old guy."

James had been standing with the skipper and turned to go saying "I've just got to get the fare off a gentleman." But when he "stepped down to the deck, he wasn't there, I walked all around."

Nevertheless, he cast off and soon the ferry was making way for Kingswear. James recalled "There was no sign of him whatsoever. I went to the wheelhouse and the skipper said 'You look like you've seen a ghost!' I said 'I think I have.'"

That same year, two further incidents occurred. "Again the weather was bad, with the boat rocking from side to side. I reached out to grab the ticket machine, which was kept in a cubby-hole, and it took off along the seating in the saloon deck, to the back of the boat." Despite the heaving water, it just didn't seem possible for such an item to jump out and slide away like that.

That cubby-hole seemed to be a focus for the haunting as the other incident involved a small bottle of diet cola that James had put in the same place for convenience and safe-keeping. One evening there were very few passengers due to the bad weather, and at the time of the incident itself there were no passengers at all, just James and the skipper in the wheelhouse. On the last journey of the night James walked through the boat to tie up the stern for the night, when he saw the bottle standing on its own right at the back of the boat on the transom.

"A couple of years ago," he added. "Another skipper saw him sat on the left hand side of the vessel, wearing black all-weather gear." And also: "Other people have seen shadows walking across the bow deck. He is usually accompanied by a musty smell, like somebody who really needs a shower — very stale."

The second time James actually saw George was in 2004. One evening he was securing the boat for the night, and was in the saloon deck locking the port door — as he turned the key in the lock his 'sixth sense' alerted him to a presence behind him. "The hairs on the back of my neck started sticking up." He felt eyes boring into the back of his neck.

"Part of my brain said 'Don't be silly, there's nothing behind you.' But the other part said 'Oh yes there is!'"

He summoned the will power to turn around and caught sight of "the back half of a person in black, disappearing from view." The deck plates were wooden and a bit creaky, but there was not a sound to give away the man's movement. Unfortunately, James had to go in exactly the same direction to get off the boat. Although he is never usually scared, he admitted he took some time to "pluck up the courage just to go and see if he was there." James dutifully went and looked, but the figure had vanished.

the wandering oarsman

An extra crew member is the subject of another nautical story told to me by Dartmouth mariner Kevin Pyne. "I'll tell you what I know," he said. "People on this river have from time to time won races at Regatta — very rarely — where there's been a stranger in the boat, and everybody thought that somebody else asked him to row. It doesn't happen so much now because people practise a lot more, but you would get a stranger on the quay and they'd row with you. And people actually won like this, and then they'd say 'Who was that?'
    "'I thought he came with you.'
    "'I thought he was your mate.'"

There may often be a perfectly innocent reason for a stranger to step in and help crew a boat in the competitions, just to make up the numbers, but on the other hand there is an old legend that just might account for it. The tale tells of the 'wreckers' who would deliberately lure a ship onto the rocks, usually in foggy or stormy weather, and then row out to seize its valuables. One such crew of nefarious oarsmen suffered a dying captain's curse.

Kevin told me "There has always been a story around the South West rowing circuit about a guy who was condemned to row the earth forever. And the story I was told was that they rowed out to salve [salvage] a boat one night which had gone on the rocks, and the captain begged them to take his young daughter and rescue her, but they were so busy plundering that they didn't want to know. And in their efforts to plunder the ship it actually came off the rock, and it drowned the lot of them. They would have probably got away if they had taken the girl, but they didn't and everybody was lost.

"The captain cursed them, and the crew of this boat can't go to heaven and can't go to hell, and the only relief they can get from anything is maybe the odd row at regattas."

"I've certainly been around boats and people have got out and people have gone 'Who was that?'

"'Oh, I don't know, I thought he came with you.'

"And they go 'Ahh!'"

Another aspect to this story is that the whole ghostly crew of the wreckers is said to be seen occasionally, all aboard a boat whose coxswain is the little girl, the captain's daughter, and she's scolding them on to row ever faster.

NavaL GHOStS

Dr Richard Porter, Curator of the museum at the Britannia Royal Naval College (BRNC), told me that one afternoon, around 4pm, some years ago, a colleague had a memorable experience on the Quarterdeck, which is the great hall on the ground floor of the college.

What he saw at first was not in the slightest unusual, simply a young woman walking across the hall. She had come from the end of the hall where the ladies toilets are situated, but he noticed that she went into classroom 04, which was unoccupied at that time. Feeling this was slightly odd, he looked in after her to check everything was all right, but there was nobody there — the room was still unoccupied.

Dr Jane Harrold, Deputy Curator of the Britannia Museum, supplemented the account, by adding "The only fatality when the college was bombed in 1942 was a petty officer Wren...[14] The only woman we know of that's been killed in the college. And that's not far from where she died, in fact, if she was going across the Quarterdeck that's almost going from one bomb to the other bomb. There were two bombs in either corner of the Quarterdeck: the bottom right hand corner where the toilets are, and the top left hand corner where 04 is."

The victim had been in the toilets when the air raid took place, the bombs causing substantial damage to the college. What prevents this story appearing in the previous chapter, is the following account by Dr Porter, which indicates an ability to influence events in the modern world.

"I was standing in the middle of the great hall, telling a colleague of mine about the ghost... the lights were off (it's normal to have the lights off at night because the side lights are on in the corridor and enough light shines through). While talking to her, all the lights on the right hand side as we're looking towards the door started to come on — one after the other: click, click, click, click, click... There was nobody standing at

---

[14] Members of the former Women's Royal Naval Service were affectionately known as Wrens after the initials WRNS.

the light switches. And then the other side. Nobody at the light switches — click, click, click, click... Every one came on, probably at half-second intervals."

They had been standing exactly where the ghost of the young woman had been seen.

Around the same time the college's Church of England chaplain spoke to a verger who knew all about the ghost. Arrangements were made for them to meet and discuss the details a few days hence. But the verger died on the eve of the meeting, and the all the information perished with him.

Another intriguing ghost story with a naval connection is located less than half a mile (0.8km) from the college, in the graveyard of the church of St Clement, Townstal. This is the mother church of the area and is older than St Saviour's church; it dates in part to the 13th century, and has traces of Norman architecture. It is notable that dedications to St Clement are frequently found in seafaring communities and his emblem is the anchor.

Late one evening a man walking up the hill from Dartmouth to Townstal ventured through the churchyard, along the path leading from Church Road. He had just passed the church door when he saw someone coming down the path towards him. As they neared each other, he noticed the figure wore full ceremonial naval uniform including a cap, sword, medals, braids, and epaulettes. The witness greeted the figure but then realised that the sailor had no face.

The next day he returned to the churchyard and, at the spot where he saw the apparition, he found the grave of a naval officer.

A remarkably similar story in the same churchyard involves another military man (loosely described as a soldier), who approached two people in the early 1980s, and asked them for a light for his cigarette. The witnesses were about to oblige when they were shocked to see he had no face. His prompt disappearance came as huge relief.

WW2 victim of 'friendly fire' accident

The Day Beacon tower (or Day Mark as it's known locally) is a prominent landmark standing some 80 feet (24m) high on the headland at Kingswear; it was built in the 1860s as a navigational aid for mariners. The site is said to be haunted by a ghost of a man who died there during the Second World War. James Thomas told me the story as he heard it from a man in a local pub one evening in the mid '90s.

The remains of a Home Guard lookout station can still be seen at Froward Point, with relics including the munitions bunker, the pinion of the big gun, as well as the spotlight and machinegun nests. According to the story, if an air raid was imminent the men stationed there would light a fire in the tower as a warning signal. A young Scotsman who was unable to sign-up for active duty, was working at the top of the tower, repairing some crumbling mortar when, as luck would have it, enemy aircraft were spotted approaching Dartmouth.

One of the Home Guard lookouts rushed up from the station at the Point and, knowing he was up there, called for the steeplejack to come down: "We've got to light the beacon!" He cried. "We've got to light the beacon!"

For whatever reason, the Scotsman refused the urgent summons, and stubbornly remained atop the vast chimney. The warden was mindful of the large number of casualties that could result if he didn't give the signal and raise the alarm so, despite his misgivings, he felt his duty was clear — he lit the beacon fire.

Unfortunately, although a long way from ground, the young man wasn't as far from harm's way as he'd supposed, and he perished ("char-grilled" was James' graphic phrase). Since then, when the wind is blowing inland from the south, on dusky winter evenings, many people have reported seeing a silhouette or dark shadow of a man standing by the Day Mark.

One man taking his evening walk noticed just such a ghostly form as the sun was sinking. The figure was motionless, with arms by its side, legs astride, and seemed to be standing about 150 yards (c.140m) away, right beside the tower.

The walker continued his journey heading for Coleton Fishacre for a short while, and looked around again. The shadowy figure was still 150 yards away, only now he too was on the trackway, but again he was just standing there, not moving at all. With hairs prickling up on the back of his neck, the man hastened along the track, but when he looked sharply around a third time and saw the silhouette still exactly the same distance away, and still absolutely motionless, he panicked and ran for his life — and didn't dare look back again.

The part about the origin of the ghost doesn't quite ring true to me (I thought the 'blackout' was the wartime rule), and I fancy it may owe more to bar-room speculation than to an historical fact; but I am in no position to judge, and James couldn't vouch for it accuracy either. That said, we are still free to accept the actual ghostly experience, whatever it may describe, at face value.

Let sleeping tigers lie?

There is a story written by J A Brooks who, while claiming its ghost to be true, admits the living character is fictitious.[15] This ambiguity is a pity because the story tells in detail how an American lieutenant, Pete G Forster of the 557th Quartermaster Railhead Company, struck up a friendship with a railway signalman at Kingswear — a companionship that seemingly continued after Pete died.

During the build-up to D-Day (Tuesday June 6th, 1944), the railway was busy with secret cargoes, and Pete often visited Tom the signalman, just to sit awhile and chat. One night Tom returned to his signal box to find Pete sitting in his usual chair, and Tom noticed that for the first time since they'd met, Pete was wearing battle uniform. Tom greeted him cheerily but Pete didn't reply. Even Tom's offer of cup of tea appeared to fall on deaf ears: Pete merely gazed up at him. Tom was wondering whether Pete was ill, when to his astonishment the young soldier simply faded away and vanished.

A scene from Operation Tiger by psychic artist Jan Polinski.

---

[15] J A Brooks 1992, *Supernatural Steam*, Norwich, Jarrold Publishing.

This quiet visitor returned the following night, and Tom grew accustomed to his being there, and even walking back to the station with him — always at night and when Tom was otherwise alone. By the end of the year the clarity of the ghost had diminished to a mere shadow, and by the beginning of 1945 Pete was simply an invisible presence. Eventually, even this sensation of being in the company of an old friend dissipated until nothing remained.

The story has a dramatic twist in that although Tom heard an official statement that Pete had been killed in action in France, his ghost first appeared over a month before D-Day, in fact it was immediately after the appalling loss of life that took place during a key military exercise codenamed Tiger.

Operation (or Exercise) Tiger lasted from the 22nd to 30th of April 1944, and was one of many in the local area during the preparations for D-Day. The wholesale evacuation of part of the South Hams had been ordered to allow Slapton Sands to be used to for top secret rehearsals of the intended Allied landings at 'Utah Beach', Normandy. Tragically, around 1:30 on the morning of Friday April 28th, nine German torpedo boats in Start Bay attacked an Allied training convoy heading for Slapton — 749 US soldiers and sailors were killed or reported as missing in action.

On a personal note, as a child playing on the beach one day I found spent WW2 rifle and machine gun ammunition as well as shrapnel from a pineapple grenade, and in 1984 I was moved when I heard rumours about the dead servicemen being buried in hastily dug mass graves in numerous parts of the local countryside. I figured that if there was any substance to the persistent claims that bodies still lay where they were unceremoniously interred in

Did these men perish together off Slapton Sands?

unmarked graves, there may be some ghosts lingering and earthbound, with a keen desire to put things right. Theirs would be a tale worth hearing, I thought. Naïvely perhaps, I mentioned this to a local journalist, who ran the story in such a way that the prospects of conducting a proper psychic investigation were, ironically, blown right out of the water.[16]

The following month, however, I met Jan Polinski who was offering psychic readings at the converted church of St Barnabas, Newcomen Road. He moved to Stoke Fleming from London ten days after my interview was published and, in just six weeks, had produced more than four hundred portraits of those killed almost exactly forty years earlier. He gave me a selection to see if I could get them published: some appeared in a local magazine,[17] and I have pleasure in including more here.

He sketched them by a process called automatic drawing, in which the conscious mind gives free rein to spontaneous impulses. Jan didn't believe he was in direct contact with the spirits of the dead, but felt able to communicate with them through living members of their family. Everybody, he told me, contains the spirits of all of their ancestors, proportionally according to the vigour of their personalities.

A medium identified this portrait as Mike of Arkansas.

I also found myself in touch with a spiritual medium living in Dartmouth, who had more conventional views regarding the independence of the spirits of the dead. She gave me the following message from one of the soldiers, a regular (as opposed to a conscript) who visited her during a private sitting.

"I am one of God's poor forgotten ones. I am Mike. I am Mike of Arkansas. I am going to get Ken to talk for me and the

[16] *Dartmouth Chronicle*, 4 May 1984.
[17] Ken Taylor 1985, Do You Know G I Graves?, *The Mouth of the Dart*, 1.

rest of us. We all feel sad at being forgotten for convenience sake by our
generals and officers who were to blame for most of our deaths. We are in
fields near the Horseman's Arms and in a corner, the left side near a
cornfield... right near is a big sort of stone building. It was a long time ago
in your time — in ours it was only yesterday so feel strongly. Bless all
those who help."[18]

The medium, who declared her belief in God and Christ, finished with a brief
message from one of the 'Great Spirits of the Universe' who are charged with
helping mankind evolve spiritually.

"I am Peacemaker and I am now with you all to give you strength and
courage for this is a fight with our U & D. They will try to form a statement
but it will not hold, and the field will be opened one day very soon now."

I still have no idea what U & D refers to, but I note that, presumably, the
passage of time for Peacemaker is similar to that for Mike — the message
was received in 1984 and so far as I know the field remains unexcavated.

The official US Department of the Navy account admits that mistakes were
made that may have contributed to the death toll of Operation Tiger, but denies
corpses remain in the area. The dead, it states, were temporarily interred
'nearby' at a WW1 military cemetery at Blackwood and then exhumed after the
end of WW2 and either returned to America at the request of their next of kin,
or transported to a dedicated WW2 cemetery at Cambridge.[19] I am sure,
however, that the Joint POW/MIA Accounting Command would like to hear of
any US servicemen whose remains may lie in unmarked graves in the South
Hams. Their motto is "Until they are home" and they have a dedicated unit
actively searching for the more than 78,000 Americans unaccounted for from
WW2 (they can be contacted via their website: www.jpac.pacom.mil).

---

[18] The reference to the Horseman's Arms is odd because there was no doubt that the
Sportsman's Arms, Hemborough Post, was actually intended (it may have been a simple
error by the scribe). The large, triangular field suspected of being the grave site can be
found at grid reference SX 831520. Many other sites have also been alleged, including the
aptly named France area on the shore of Slapton Ley.
[19] Operational Archives Naval Historical Centre 2000, *Exercise Tiger*,
http://www.history.navy.mil/faqs/faq20-1.htm .

a white lady, and a murderer

Tudor House, 5 Higher Street, Dartmouth, also apparently held a spirit that was unable to leave until a medium intervened; and there are also sightings of a white lady here. Now a restaurant, this is one of the best of the remaining timber-framed houses developed for Dartmouth's wealthy 17th century merchants. Its façade reputedly features the windows from the captain's quarters of a Spanish galleon, and the building's foundations are thought to be 15th century or even earlier.

The tales I heard in the 1980s about this building with its slightly sloping rooms with their low ceilings, suggest that apart from a lot of spooky creaking and a door on the top floor that inexplicably slammed shut and refused to reopen, the resident ghost was actually rather charming. The white lady used to walk up the stairs carrying a candle and, when she reached the very top, she would simply vanish.

Rather like the grey lady of The Cherub, it is fascinating to imagine how such an apparently trivial action could have left such an indelible mark on the spiritual fabric of the house — perhaps it was simply years of repetition by a woman who cherished a deep and abiding love of her home. What marks this white lady as more than a shade will be seen shortly.

This building once served as Dartmouth's Job Centre and, when it closed in 1990, the local newspaper carried an interesting interview with South Hams manager Mike Gurney.[20] He played down the haunting saying that nothing had been reported in recent years, but he admitted that there had formerly been a ghost problem that had clearly worried staff. The disturbances seemed to be concentrated in the upper storeys where the manager's office was situated. People living across the road also reported seeing a figure wandering around in the building when it should have been empty.

The vacant building was bought by Nigel Way who recalls visiting the property shortly afterwards. He told me "That was the one time I would most definitely say that I had an [inexplicable] experience. That was just between the 2nd floor and 3rd floor of the place: there's a spiral staircase that's pretty old.... We were going around (myself, the architect, guy from the listed buildings, and my wife)... going up to look at the top floor. We were picking our way over it very carefully, it was almost derelict, there were lots of broken windows, the top two floors hadn't been used for a number of years... there were floorboards missing, there were rotten floorboards...

Blackdown Rings hillfort (see previous double page spread and pages 96,107,108).

---

[20] *Dartmouth Chronicle*, 25 May 1990.

"I really felt this definite hand on my chest pushing me backwards... We cut the visit fairly short after that... came out and the architect said 'are you alright?' I said 'I feel a bit strange', and she said 'I think I felt exactly the same thing as you did.'"

In due course the building became a dedicated seafood restaurant called Hooked. In or around 2000 'soul rescuer' Terry O'Sullivan was called in by its proprietor Mark Coxon. The visit was organised with the BBC, and Terry was accompanied by an interviewer with a camera (sadly, it seems the tapes were not broadcast).

Terry, who runs workshops at the College of Psychic Studies in London, felt that "Just inside the door someone had been murdered, and that person was still there, earthbound on the site." When he announced this to Mark, the proprietor pointed at the nearby circular table and said (in Terry's words) "a customer sitting in the chair on this spot asked to be moved because she felt freaked-out by the atmosphere."

Terry told me "My job is not just to locate in the same way that Derek Acorah does on Living TV.[21] Derek is a good bloke and excellent at what he does, very genuine and good at his job. The difference is that he's a clairvoyant, clairaudient psychic who is able to detect earthbound spirits to communicate with them. He's not in the business of removing them. People pay me to remove them. That's what I went to do."

He was shown around each room on the lower floors, and pronounced whether there was "any impact caused by influence" or whether the room was "clear". There were, he discovered, quite a few spirits present.

"The atmosphere was volatile." He recalled. "There would have been a number of activities over the years. Throughout its term of history the memories and manifestations loop through time becoming active again. This is why I really wanted to get my teeth into the full job and needed access to all the space."

He had arranged to have unlimited access to the whole building in order to 'cleanse' it thoroughly so that no spirits remained, but at the last minute he was told that he could only operate on the ground and first floors.

"I did my best," he told me, "to move the spirits on, but because I couldn't access the top I didn't have the run of the property to do a proper job. I couldn't guarantee the job had been done. I told Mark I was happy to come back. But the call didn't come."

Terry did, however, manage to help the spirit of the murdered person who had been upsetting the atmosphere in the ground floor restaurant. The spirit had apparently, and not altogether unnaturally, been harbouring a profound sense of injustice.

---

[21] E.g. the popular show *Most Haunted*, which Derek Acorah left at Halloween 2005.

To deal with the murdered person Terry used the 'Stairway to Heaven' technique, which involves making a "link with the light." He focussed on the sun "using the old pagan tradition of the sun being the father god — simply a form of light, a symbol of light. You could call it the Paradise Road, or Heaven.

"It is," he continued, "about moving the spirit from the dense world of the astral; changing the vibration of the earth-bound spirit's density — to lighten it."

"Neat pun!" I quipped, and Terry agreed.

"Connect with the sun," he said. "From the sun within, using your power of thought, create a bridge or stairway of light which you consciously manifest to the earth (physical) level. Then call the ancestors, loved ones, or angels. And, in the recognition that there is someone on that stairway that they can identify with, a switch in consciousness takes place and, instead of thinking about their own interests, they say 'I wonder what they're up to?' And that's enough motivation to send them on.

"The murdered person was," he said, "happy to move on."

But that wasn't the end of matters. "The real fun began after midnight... you could feel a lot of activity taking place. The BBC man was completely freaking out. He was trying to sleep but just as he was dozing off he was awakened by bad dreams of things getting at him. So he wouldn't sleep in the room unless I was in there with him. In the morning the atmosphere felt quite calm — there was a significant difference to the feeling of the restaurant in the hours of light and darkness."

Terry felt that the disturbed atmosphere spread beyond the house itself. "There are lines," he explained, "like the threads of a spider web, that are like tributaries feeding into ley lines, which are like arteries. Web lines can have deposits in them of negative influence which don't always remain still, and as they move so the atmosphere moves with them."

A couple of years later, in 2002, Mark invited the Torbay Investigators of the Paranormal (TIP[22]) to hold a vigil there. So, on the evening of Saturday February 9th, TIP's chairman and founder member, David Phillips, and two fellow TIP members were given free access to the premises, and were left alone in the building for the night. The team decided to investigate the building from the bottom upwards, and positioned three video cameras on the ground floor. An hour later, with nothing paranormal to report, they moved their equipment onto the first floor.

Here, one of David's colleagues noted his video camera had filmed some orbs floating around, but these were not clearly defined and, as David told me, although some orbs are "possible spirit manifestations" they often have purely natural causes (but more of orbs in a moment). At around 2:30am they judged it was time to move up to the second floor, and it was at this point that the other member of the team left to go home.

---

[22]http://www.tipfiles.com .

The second floor consisted of a flat with a kitchen, bathroom, and bedroom. At that time it was both unoccupied and unfurnished, but there were marks on the floor that betrayed where the bed had been, and David placed his camera with a good view of that area. This decision was based on a story the manager had told them about a former tenant who had developed a physical illness. Sometimes, the tenant had been lying down when the ghostly lady appeared and sat on the bed beside them as if to tend to their well-being, and giving them the comfort of company at a distressing time. It is this tender-hearted interaction that distinguishes this haunting from a simple repeating pattern — it demonstrates conscious intent and, indeed, compassion.

It was between 3 o'clock and 4am (when the human body is most desperate for sleep, and the mind is most likely to play tricks on the unwary, which is why TIP's recording equipment is so important) that David's camera filmed orbs "little balls of transparent light" as he described them, which seemed to fly in straight lines near floor level. Unfortunately, the tapes were of insufficient quality for any useful images to be included here.

By 5:30am everything had quietened down, and they stopped recording when their tapes were full. David started to review the videotapes they had made during the night. Then "we heard the sound of a key in the lock, the side door opening and someone coming up the stairs." In the quiet of the pre-dawn Sunday morning, they clearly heard the sound of footsteps ascending all the way from the ground floor to the second, but when David's colleague went to investigate, he returned saying "There was no-one there." Had they caught the sounds on tape it should have been possible to identify whether the door was the wooden side door (which they assumed it to be), a door in an adjoining building, or a phantom door with no modern counterpart.

a smile as sweet as life itself

Our next story introduces us to a gentle spirit quietly offering a message of hope and support to the living. The Gunfield in Castle Road, Dartmouth, is an elegant 19th century building located in a picturesque position with the Dart at the bottom of its garden, and it may be host to the sweetest haunting in the town. She is a peaceful spirit with an enchanting smile, and seems to date from an early period in the history of the house when it was still a private dwelling.

For much of the 20th century The Gunfield operated as a hotel, and a young woman guest in the first half of the that century saw the figure of a grey-haired old lady in the large mirror in the entrance hall. The old lady appeared to come right through the mirror and step out into the hall. The ghost then casually walked up the stairs as far as the landing, where she turned and gave the young woman below an unforgettably beautiful smile. The old lady then simply faded from sight.

Since then at least five people have been captivated by this otherworldly visitor's bewitching friendliness. Mrs Lusher told me of her experience, which occurred around 1950 when she saw the old lady arranging flowers in a vase. The lady was dressed in fashionable clothes from the 1920s era, including a long skirt, a jacket and blouse, and a straw hat. When the ghost became aware she was being watched, she gave her a beaming smile that the witness described as having a "timeless quality."

Two young children who slept in a four-poster bed in a small, almost square room with a conical ceiling, repeatedly told their parents (who were the hotel's owners) that an old lady came and told them bedtime stories. The parents thought little of the youngsters' statements until one night, when their mother secretly peeked in on them. Both children were wide awake and seemed to be listening contentedly to someone that she herself could neither see not hear. From that point on it was impossible to merely dismiss the incidents as childish imagination.

Another time, a young married couple were staying in what was then Room One when a grey-haired old lady entered their room, gave them a wonderfully charming smile, and silently departed. They assumed the uninvited but unobtrusive visitor was a guest at the hotel who had become lost and was searching for her own room. It was only at breakfast the next morning that the happy couple discovered they had actually been blessed with a smile from the kindly old soul whose spirit embodied the charm of the old Gunfield hotel itself.

RAISING the DEAD

The following two accounts are of unusual interest as they tell of impromptu exorcisms. The events of the first story took place during the winter of 1980 in rented accommodation on Victoria Road, in a building dating to the late Georgian era (the lower part of this road was built in a valley bottom that had been occupied by a tidal inlet, which had been filled following an Improvement Act in 1815).

A local woman in her mid twenties was troubled by a spate of odd occurrences such as a collection of pottery ornaments rattling, her TV shaking, and the drum of a spin dryer spinning even though it was unplugged. One night she felt she'd had enough and addressed the budding poltergeist (literally 'noisy ghost') firmly, asking it to leave her in peace.

Later, a friend who lived nearby asked her about the man who was with her that night. The neighbour had seen our young woman through the window, talking to a middle aged man in a brown suit. This casual comment not only provides a valuable independent visual record of the unofficial and otherworldly tenant, but demonstrates how easy it can be to see a ghost without even realising it.

Some people might have thought about vacating the premises after this, but our resident had an artistic temperament and trusted her intuition. The spirit was not, she felt, evil or frightening, but sad. Something bound him to the earth, yet he was desperately unhappy here and desired nothing more than to find a way to leave and be free.

Things settled down after that. She had recognised his presence and they had come to an understanding. Then a new man entered her life. Although he was a stranger to Dartmouth he was no stranger to paranormal phenomena, and he seems to have acted as a catalyst because one night in January 1981 a remarkable event took place.

It began when she felt the ghostly presence enter the living room (as often happened). She felt his sorrow, but still could not help. This time though, instead of using her habitual mental block to dissuade the spirit from manifesting in any way, she allowed him free rein. At this point her boyfriend was suddenly overwhelmed with feelings of unutterable loneliness and despair. Hot tears rose unbidden to his eyes as he gazed directly into the darkness of the ghost's existence in the nether void. He had become a medium for the ghost's desolate soul to express its abject misery.

Crucially, the artistic instincts of his girlfriend rose to meet the needs of this strange occasion. She found her imagination conjuring a blasted tree in a wasteland, a tree whose branches could serve as a ladder. Then she kept a careful eye on a shrouded figure, the ghost itself, as it ascended the tree.

The intensity of effort in their earnest attempt to help liberate the earth-bound soul is hard to convey, and the outcome was as much a surprise to them as it still seems to me. As she watched the spirit approach the top of that sacred tree she saw a great black hand appear from the sky and reach down to it. At that moment an impenetrable veil mantled the scene, and the aching distress that had wracked the novice medium lifted. There was no doubt in their minds that the spirit had found peace. And, indeed, there was no further disturbance in the property.

Anthony Hemmings told me the following memorable anecdote that, although lacking its imaginative details, has strong parallels with the foregoing exorcism. These events took place in a block of flats at Windsor Road, Townstal: the man in the flat above had died, and soon afterwards Anthony's friend answered a knock at his door only to find the dead man standing there. All he could think of to say was "You don't live in this flat, you live upstairs" and promptly shut the door.

The same thing happened several times, and he always repeated the words "You don't live here, you live upstairs." The message eventually seems to have struck a chord as the ghost ceased to appear — perhaps the ghost did finally ascend, not merely to a higher storey but to a higher spiritual plane.

CHAPTER THREE

SPIRITS

HOSTS of the DEAD ARE NOT the ONLY types of SUPERNATURAL PHENOMENA INVESTIGATED BY a DEDICATED RESEARCHER INTO the PARANORMAL, AND NOW we SHOULD extend OUR TOUR to INCLUDE a WIDE VARIETY of OTHER WEIRD events that COMBINE to make the DARTMOUTH ENVIRONS SUCH a fascinating place. Leaving BEHIND the SOULS of PEOPLE AND OTHER ANIMALS, as WELL as ALL the PARAPHERNALIA SUCH as CLOTHES, CARRIAGES, AND BUILDINGS that accompany these GHOSTS of the past, we may NOW DELVE INTO SOMEWHAT DEEPER mysteries WHERE we SHALL ENCOUNTER BEINGS AND SPIRITUAL forces that NEVER INHABITED a PHYSICAL BODY (HUMAN OR OTHERWISE). We are PROBABLY most familiar with the ANGELS AND DEVILS of CHRISTIAN MYTHOLOGY, BUT there are OTHER, OLDER DENIZENS of the SPIRITUAL REALMS, AND we SHALL meet SOME IN DARTMOUTH.

THE CLOCK THAT STRIKES 13

I was talking to a correspondent on the telephone, when I heard his clock strike the quarter hour in the background, and I commented on the musical chimes. "Don't start me on that" he replied. "We called it the Dead Clock. It chimes thirteen times when someone in the family is going to die, and always stops at the time of their death."

It's an old-fashioned, mahogany, wall-mounted clock, and it had been in his family for at least half a century. His grandmother had told him about the legend ever since he was a child many years ago.

One day he visited her home as usual, but found that she had died. The doctor examined her and told him how long she had been dead — a glance at the clock showed it had stopped at the exact time of her death. The Dead Clock maintained its uncanny time-keeping in two UK cities before it was brought to Dartmouth, where its reputation

The angle tower, Dartmouth Castle (see page 78).

continues. I am particularly grateful to this witness for allowing me to publish the details of his remarkable story, and I am happy to respect his desire for anonymity: few publications are given the chance to include tales of such a sensitive and personal nature.

magical charms

Sympathetic magic lies at the heart of a superstition current in Cornworthy in the mid 19th century. In or around 1848 the local vicar received an odd request and, sensing that it bore the hallmark of unchristian beliefs, he determined to teach his parishioner (and his man-servant) a lesson in gullibility.

The servant had a horse that he felt was at risk of going lame with a festering foot. He drew out a nail from the afflicted foot (whether this nail was the cause of the wound, or merely a normal horseshoe nail is unclear), and scoured his wits for what to do with it — this iron nail was the key to the horse's recovery. The charm relied on preventing the nail from rusting: if it rusted the horse's wound would become infected, but if it remained untarnished, the wound would clear up (this is the opposite of the popular wart-charming notion that rubbing a wart with meat and burying it causes the wart to decay and disappear as the meat rots in the ground).

Believing the vicar to be both the wisest and most dependable man around, the servant entrusted him with the safekeeping of the precious amulet. But although the vicar appeared to accept the commission, he actually broke faith with his servant, and secretly placed it in a situation where persistent damp would be sure to rust the nail in no time.

Fortunately for the vicar, the horse made a full recovery, and the nail was produced for examination. Now thoroughly corroded, it was held up as evidence of the folly of this rustic superstition. Whether the servant was instantly converted to his master's belief system is unclear; the Rev S G Harris who recorded this account,[1] certainly doubted it.

Sympathetic magic is said to operate because of a magical bond or linkage between things. The voodoo doll is probably the most widely known example of sympathetic magic: the doll is completely inert until the practitioner makes a magical connection with the intended victim — usually by affixing something uniquely personal such as a lock of hair, nail clippings, or even a thread from their clothes. Then and only then, whatever happens to the doll is believed to affect the victim.

There is a wealth of anecdotal evidence to suggest that this technique can produce real, physical effects in the victim, but western science invokes the power of suggestion as the causative agent rather than the powers of the spirit world. If the victim believes

---

[1] Rev S G Harris 1885, Eighth Report of the Committee on Devonshire Folklore, *Transactions of the Devonshire Association*, 17, 119.

— even subconsciously — in the power of the curse, his fears would undermine his self-confidence, nervousness would cause him to become accident prone, and the psychosomatic feedback loop that governs our immune system would be compromised. Moreover, as each ingredient in this seething cauldron of woes takes its toll, the victim inexorably spirals ever more deeply into its sinister spell.

Although it is popularly assumed that such practices can only be used for evil, the same type of magic can be used to bring healing, as in the case of the Cornworthy nail charm: by protecting the nail from harm (rusting) the horse is also saved. But how, we might ask, could such a charm, or rather the power of suggestion, affect a horse? One could make a case for the servant's positive outlook being able to communicate itself to a creature as sensitive as a horse, which would argue that the true magic resided in the man's belief, rather than in the nail (he must have been devastated by the vicar's subterfuge) — the placebo effect is a modern equivalent. But I fear the truth of the matter may be simply that, like most warts, most injuries clear up in time, all by themselves, especially if the immune system is kept healthy with an optimistic and confident approach to life.

A more direct use of sympathetic magic for healing was recorded by William Pengelly who interviewed the parents of a previously sick child in May 1877 at Kingswear.[2] Their baby girl had been born 'ruptured' on Wednesday November 3rd, 1875, and a folk remedy was seized upon as her best chance of a cure. Perhaps it was because her father was a carpenter that the charm involved an ash tree, but he didn't perform the ritual himself (in fact he was somewhat disinterested in the superstition). Instead, an 'experienced' old man living in Kingswear arranged for another man to assist him, and they went together to Hoodown Wood a short distance to the north of the village.

There, the old man selected a 'maiden' tree — one that had been not been dealt with by any man, either in planting or by coppicing etc. With the help of his assistant or apprentice perhaps, the upright trunk of the young ash tree was pierced, and together they used wedges to carefully split the wood vertically, but not so far as to reach the top of the tree, which was left intact.

With the tree suitably prepared, the old man, the child (who was then eleven weeks old), her mother, and another woman went into the wood on the afternoon of Tuesday January 18th, 1876 (the date was written down by the child's thoughtful grandmother). With the split tree held open, the baby was passed through it headfirst. The person who caught her on the other side passed her around to their left-hand side, so that the child would "go round with the sun" (i.e. deosil). This was repeated so that the girl passed through the open ash tree three times in all.

---

[2] William Pengelly et al 1884, On Devonshire Folk-lore, *Transactions of the Devonshire Association*, 16, 94.

Then the halves of the tree were brought together and nailed tightly closed. The belief was that as the tree healed so would the child. Many children (but up until that time, only boys) had undergone the same ceremony at the hands of the old man, who never sought nor received any payment for his services, and who had performed the rite for as long as anyone could remember.

William went to the wood and found two trees that showed the scars of having been used in this way. On the basis of the mother's description of the location, he believed he had found the very one used for the girl, and said it "was nine inches [23cm] in circumference at the centre of the slit, where neither the bark nor wood had completely closed." The scar, he added, was about seven feet (2.1m) long. The other tree had twice the circumference, and the scar was of comparable length although its wood was completely closed: the bark, however, was still about two and a half inches (6.4cm) apart at the centre.

The girl was, at the time of William's visit, perfectly well, but the old man had died and, unless he left a fully trained assistant, his knowledge of charms perished with him. I can think of two good reasons why ash might have been selected as the best tree for this ritual: firstly the tree is robust and very good at healing itself; and secondly the young tree has a tall, straight trunk. The fact that ash also has a strong association with the pagan Anglo Saxon god of magic — Woden (Odin) — may be coincidental.

Another instance of the use of the power of sympathetic magic occurred at Dittisham, and was reported in the local press in 1869.[3] The reporter held the view that witchcraft was very much in evidence in the village, and presented the following instance as one of many examples. The alleged victims were pigs belonging to a reputable publican, and several had perished in unusual circumstances. He was advised that a local witch was to blame, and that he needed to use a particular charm to defend himself and his property from her ill wishes. Accordingly, he took up one of the dead pigs, and cut out its heart. Then he stuck the heart all over with pins, and placed it in front of his fire, where he left it until it was charred throughout and burned to a cinder.

Although it might appear that the pins and burning were acting against the pig, we must remember that it was the witch who had (allegedly) hexed the animal and caused its heart to stop. Therefore her influence had acted on the heart and, if prompt action was taken, her evil magic could still be lingering in the heart — and that was the link between the witch herself and the ritual destruction of the charm. Whether the publican's livestock fared any better after this severe self-defence charm was performed wasn't stated, neither was the effect (if any) upon the local witch.

We may note that many advertising campaigns use our seemingly instinctive trust in sympathetic magic to exploit us: a common example is that having a sexy car will, as if by osmosis, boost our own virility and status; or that eating a certain breakfast

---

[3] R Burnet Morris 1928, Devonshire Folk-Lore, *Transactions of the Devonshire Association*, 60, 121. *The Western Times*, May 25 1869.

cereal will make our whole lives more exciting. Keep your eyes open and you'll spot many more fascinating modern examples of these dark arts.

There is a public house in Dartmouth that is reputedly protected by a magical charm — a dead mouse wrapped in a ten-shilling note. This bizarre charm was found during renovations following a fire; it had been hidden in a hole in a wall of the main bar of the Seven Stars in Smith Street. It is still kept in a nook of the timber beams, and the legend says that its protective power will vanish if it is ever removed from the premises.

It is notable that although in decimal currency, a 10s note equates to a mere 50p, when it was in circulation in the 1960s perhaps, it would have paid for a good night out, so whoever created the charm was certainly in earnest about what they were doing rather than flippantly creating it for a joke.

The frail mouse that guards the Seven Stars.

Although the note features the figure of Britannia, the eponymous spirit of the British Isles that is fêted locally in the naming of the Britannia Royal Naval College, it is difficult to credit her with any direct involvement in the charm. The significance of the mouse is another mystery — was it a sacrificial victim, or did its mummification attempt to mitigate its accidental slaying? Was the charmer (presumably the publican at the time) attempting to ward off an infestation of vermin? The charm is fragile with age so I am particularly grateful to landlord Mike Priest and barmaid Chloe for showing it to me, and I hope this photograph will satisfy most people's curiosity, allowing the original to rest in peace, spreading whatever gentle magic it can.

MODERN WITCHES AND PRE-CHRISTIAN WORSHIP

Some modern magicians regard the forces they seek to control as impersonal, natural energies that are, like electricity, inherently dangerous but with great potential for good. Many other people, particularly those attracted to the path of Wicca, believe the world to be inhabited by sentient deities — gods and goddesses that share their secret powers with the faithful.

One night in 1970, a teenager born and bred in Dartmouth was out and about, and chanced to roam out to Dartmouth Castle, Castle Road. There, around midnight, she was astonished to find a sky-clad (naked) coven of witches engaged in their sabbat rites within the ruin's walls. She observed them discretely for some time, and later learned that a coven had been well known to operate in the Dartmouth area since the early 1960s at least, and it (or another like it) also held sabbats at the prehistoric earthworks near Halwell Cross.

It should be noted, however, that almost all contemporary British covens are known to be modern, and their rituals are 20th century in origin. Moreover, it would be extremely unlikely for a traditional coven (if such could have persisted through the centuries of Christian persecution) to pursue their religious rites at a secular site such as Dartmouth Castle.

It is far more likely that these particular revellers were mostly thrill-seekers engaged in a personal revolt against the strictures of conventional behaviour. Indeed, the ruinous state of the ditched curtain wall and angle tower (see page 73) built in the 14th century by Mayor John Hauley[4] makes a fitting backdrop to a sabbat dedicated to the decay of state authority. However, the dilapidated tower and wall are relics are of the oldest parts of Dartmouth Castle, and the castle's more recent elements (it was still manned in World War Two) are likely to remain in a much better state of preservation — especially now the site enjoys the patronage of English Heritage.

That said, we may note that the adjacent church of St Petrox is much older than the castle, and also older than its current fabric (dated to 1641) suggests: a deed of 1192 mentions a monastery here, although it may originally have been little more than a solitary hermit's cell that had accumulated an aura of sanctity. There is also a persistent tradition that the Christian edifice was deliberately situated above a primordial holy spring whose waters run into the Dart from below the platform on which the church was founded. Such a spring would almost certainly have been believed to have healing properties. A natural spring beside the church of St Thomas at Kingswear, was apparently regarded as a holy well and used as a wishing well, and another holy well is said to have existed beside a medieval chapel, now demolished, below Dyer's Wood, Dartmouth. And, of course, the village of Halwell owes its very name to the Old English words 'holy spring'.

The cross on the Devon Flag is dedicated to St Petroc as a result of a series of recurring dreams in which local man Kevin Pyne visited the church of St Petrox. In 2002 he was lying gravely ill in Derriford Hospital, Plymouth, while the design of the flag was being debated on BBC Radio Devon. Hovering between life and death, the dreams were significant to his recovery, and strengthened him through that time, in recognition for which he successfully campaigned for the saint to be commemorated by the flag.

Early Christianity zealously supplanted pagan sites and practices with its own structures and rites, as confirmed by an infamous instruction to St Augustine issued by Pope Gregory in 601. Regarding ways of eradicating indigenous

---

[4] Hauley (also written Hawley) met Geoffrey Chaucer in 1373 and is believed to have been that author's inspiration for 'The Shipman' in *The Canterbury Tales*. Hauley's memorial brass, which is hailed as one of the most important in Devon, is in the chancel of the church of St Saviour (he died in 1408); he was also the greatest donor to the building fund for that church.

religion, Gregory advised that pagan sanctuaries should be seized and "cleansed with holy water, have altars set up in them, and relics deposited there."

The church at Dartmouth Castle is named after Abbot Petroc who lived in a hermitage on Bodmin Moor and died in 594. By the Middle Ages he was pre-eminent among Celtic saints, and bizarre and fanciful legends circulated about his life. Perhaps the naming of the church in memory of a native saint, and one who followed the Celtic style of worship (very different from the Roman model), was an indelible recognition of the fact that the holy spring had been venerated for generations before Christianity came to these shores.

The proximity of the enigmatic Galions Boure (later called Gallants Bower) may also have been influential in allowing local religious beliefs to endure here despite the inroads of the evangelical Middle Eastern faith. If that is the case, then it is just possible that our teenager actually witnessed a ritual reclaiming of the site in the name of the native pagan gods.

When you start looking for something, it's not unusual to find it. That sentence states the obvious to an absurd degree, yet the sentiments are famously endorsed in the Sermon on the Mount: "seek and ye shall find", and we all know it holds water. But, when you start looking for something occult, what you find is usually a clue to a deeper mystery. What, for instance, can we make of Dartmouth's disappearing white rabbit?

William Pengelly[5] described how the creature defied capture despite the efforts of determined hunters. Even when its pursuers literally leaped upon it and believed it to be caught beneath their bodies, it simply vanished from their grasp only to reappear "ever so far away."

# of HARES AND GOATS

This could merely be a case of a freak albino rabbit that evaded capture due to the superstitious fears of its hunters. When we're afraid, even subconsciously, we often fail at the last moment to grasp the nettle — many an opportunity slips through our fingers when we lack self-confidence.

Incidentally, this ghostly creature is a recurrent and widely distributed motif that may be interpreted in the light of native religion. The hare is a native species (in contrast to the rabbit) and has long been associated with the moon — its image can be seen silhouetted in the disc of the full moon (it often helps to squint a bit!).[6] The quest to grasp the moon is a recurring theme in Celtic mythology, and that moon-white hare was certainly an unreachable goal of the ancient Celts.

---

[5] William Pengelly et al 1884, On Devonshire Folk-lore, *Transactions of the Devonshire Association*, 16, 98.

[6] Try not to be too distracted by the image of the yin/yang symbol, which is particularly prominent in the mornings following the full moon.

The tradition that a goat haunts the wood on Dyer's Hill, which rises steeply to the northwest of Warfleet, may be a straightforward sighting of the ghost of a dead goat, or maybe it could also be part of Dartmouth's pagan heritage. It is largely because of the Celt's pantheistic veneration for the Horned God — Herne, or Cernunnos, the Lord of the Greenwood — that the goat is still popularly associated with the Devil at Satanic rites (it is important to note though, that Celtic worship was not devoted to black magic but was holistic and pragmatic). The legend of the goat could be a warning couched in the language of symbols, as is normal in occultism. In this instance it could be saying: "Beware of this place, it's the site of the witches' sabbat, where the spirit of the Horned God reveals itself."

witches of tudor dartmouth

Margareta Foxe not only denied that she was a witch but denied that witches could wield the powers popularly accredited to them. However, there were sufficient people who bore witness against her for her to be formally accused by the diocese of Exeter. She was summoned from her home in Townstal to be judged by the ecclesiastical Consistory Court in Exeter on Wednesday September 28th, 1558.

Her trial took place against a backdrop of religious intolerance: the reigning monarch was Mary I, the devout Catholic queen whose reign saw the revival of medieval laws allowing heretics to be executed and their property seized, a law she infamously exploited — earning the epithet Bloody Mary for her zeal that led more than 275 people being burned at the stake for heresy. Although Henry VIII's 1542 law against witch practices had been repealed in 1547 by his successor Edward VI, Edward actually introduced new legislation in 1551 to toughen penalties against witches, and those charged with causing death by spells and incantations were on trial for their lives. Although witchcraft was not directly linked with heresy (meaning that in England witches were hanged rather than burned), a suspected witch was still in very serious trouble in Mary's reign.

A transcript of parts of the trial has been published,[7] but this does not include the charges brought against her, nor the verdict, but only some of her answers to the interrogation. However, we can glean some facts about her situation. For instance, we may envisage her as a middle aged woman whose parents had been dead for some 27 years, and she had an eight-year-old daughter. Margareta had been born in Malborough to William and Elenora Gudgyn, and had subsequently lived at Modbury, Woodleigh, and Cornwood before moving to Townstal, where she lived for just a few months before her ordeal.

She maintained that both she and her mother-in-law Joane Foxe had been slandered by Elenore Coxworthy of Modbury, who had branded them witches. Margareta went

---

[7] Todd Gray and John Draisey 1992, Witchcraft in the Diocese of Exeter: Part II, *Devon and Cornwall Notes and Queries*, XXXVI, 281.

so far as to say that part of the reason she had moved around so much since then was that the allegation of witchcraft had followed her from place to place, making normal life impossible. This protracted campaign of defamation was apparently encouraged by the vicar of Blackawton who, she had heard, summoned a man called Owyn (also known as Lang) to testify that his illness had been caused by her supernatural arts. Fortunately for her, although he was summoned to see the vicar three times, Owyn steadfastly refused to collaborate in this accusation, and had been content to regard his sickness as a purely natural consequence of his hunting woodcocks by night.

Another of the charges against her was alleged by Robert Lessetour of Townstal, who, among others, accused her of intending to kill his cattle by witchcraft. Again, she denied the defamation, and said she believed it was God's own plague that had made the beasts sicken and die.

Apparently the issue was not resolved at that hearing, as she was also brought before the court on Tuesday October 25th. Whether or not she had spent the intervening weeks in gaol, I imagine the serious nature of the charges would have deprived her of much comfort. However, she maintained her defence that the testimony against her was mere slander. She also replied to questioning that although she had heard that witches could stop cows producing milk, she did not believe witches could actually do such things.

When natural causes for unusual events are not known, it is all too easy for human insecurity and fear to find release in the form of a scapegoat, particularly a newcomer to the community. Although it is possible that Margareta was a truly evil person and used subtle methods to injure her neighbours' cows, I personally find her replies rational and consistent, and trust that she was acquitted of the charges.

I fear no such escape could have awaited the three subjects of a later inquiry — husband and wife Michael and Alice Trevisard and their son Peter, all of Hardnesse.[8] Anti-witchcraft laws had been tightened under Elizabeth I when, in 1562, the use of witchcraft for any intent or purpose came to be considered worthy of the death penalty. The use of torture to extract confessions from suspected witches was, however, not legally sanctioned in England (although abuses occurred).

Eleven witnesses gave depositions against the Trevisard family over a period of six months in 1601 and 1602, enough to make the sheer weight of public opinion against them seem damning. The legal system accepted as fact the idea that witches could exercise real magical power to harm people and property, so the mixture of anecdote and circumstantial evidence (outlined below) given against this family could well have been sufficient to convict them.

---

[8] Hardnesse was one of several largely seafaring communities that are now combined in the town of Dartmouth; it lay to the north of the deep tidal inlet that was filled in the 19th century and accommodates the market square.

Transcripts of the depositions made to Sir Thomas Ridgewaye, knight and a Justice of the Peace for Devon, have been published[9] and show that the allegations were of the gravest kind. Given the enthusiasm with which witchcraft trials were prosecuted, I strongly suspect that Thomas and Alice at least were sent to the gallows for the capital crime of murder by witchcraft (the closing years of Queen Elizabeth I's reign saw a surge in the persecution of witches, and this accelerated further when James I took the throne: in this ten-year period almost half of all those accused of murdering by witchcraft were hanged by order of Home Circuit judges). I may be wrong about their fate, but I somehow doubt Dartmouth bucked the trend.

Even the summary of the depositions below gives an authentic flavour of the paranoia that was not only sweeping England but had ironically already brought hell-on-Earth to many parts of the Continent.

twelve depositions

On Friday October 2nd, 1601 (the same date applies to all the depositions until stated otherwise), William Tompson, a seaman of Dartmouth, said that around Michaelmas (September 29th) in or about 1595, he was with Robert Furseman on the foss[10] at midnight when they met somebody wearing a grey cape with the hood pulled down so low as to be unrecognisable. They issued a challenge, and discovered it was Alice. They parted, but not on good terms, and when William promptly tripped and nearly broke his neck in the fall, she laughed at him. He recovered himself and struck her with his musket rod, at which she threatened him, saying it would have been better if he'd never met her. Three weeks later he set out to sea, and the vessel inexplicably caught fire and sank with the loss of 18 of its crew of 24. Although he survived, he was rescued by a Portuguese vessel and imprisoned in Spain for a year. Upon his return he again met Alice, who said he'd be back in prison there again within another year — and just six months later he was indeed captured and imprisoned by the Spaniards, for two years.

Johan Laishe of Hardnesse said that about 1595 she'd refused to give Alice a drink of ale, and Alice said she'd reduce her to poverty. Two days later a barrel of ale suddenly jumped up from where it had been standing and fell, emptying all its contents on the ground.

Susan Tooker of Hardnesse said that in around 1597 Alice said she'd see Susan lose all her wealth. Susan's husband was at sea at that time and, in fair weather, his ship and all its

[9] Todd Gray 1992, Witchcraft in the Diocese of Exeter: Dartmouth, *Devon and Cornwall Notes and Queries*, XXXVI, 230.
[10] This was an artificial causeway built by the 13th century that connected Hardnesse with Clifton on the other side of the tidal inlet; a mill set in it was powered by tidal energy. Modern Foss Street follows its course.

cargo were lost. She added that once she had refused Peter a drink, and he told her it would have been better if she had given it. The next day she fell ill and continued sick for seven weeks. She also told how Mayor Martyn's new timber store at Hardnesse was criticised by Michael, who said it would blow away. Sure enough, it did, and every time they fixed it, it was wrecked again. They moved it to a more sheltered location, but it was still ravaged. Moreover, the men that had worked on the timber store were also sailors, and they were all cast away on their next voyage.

Johan Baddaford of Hardnesse recalled Alice Trevisard telling her (Johan's) husband that he would need to go to Pursever Wood and regain his sanity. A few weeks later he sailed to La Rochelle (aboard the Dittisham vessel *Hope*) and returned raving and out of his mind, and remained in that condition for two years. Alice also told Johan that she would be bankrupt within seven years, and although she was then fairly wealthy then, at the time of the deposition she was indeed penniless. Johan added that during Lent 1598 she had washed some clothes for Alice and asked for a penny as payment. Alice eventually handed her the money but said she wouldn't benefit from it. Johan bought some drink with the money but fell ill before she could drink it; she remained sick for seven weeks.

One Monday within a year of that illness, Johan and some neighbours had visited Sir Ridgewaye at his home in Townstal to complain against Alice, and they had met her on the way back down. Alice told Johan that someone in her family would soon be burned. She was so frightened that she didn't dare light a fire for several days. Then, on Thursday, she set some coals in her fireplace, with her son sitting at the hearth, and had turned away to get some wood to help kindle the fire when she heard the child screaming. The collar around his neck was in flames. He was burned to the bone, and died three weeks later. Johan maintained that the fire had not been lit at the time.

Alice Butler of Hardnesse said that around Christmas 1599 she was sitting at Hardnesse with Michael Trevisard, and chanced to comment that she wished her child could run as well as the other children. Michael told her, and repeated the statement until she could bear it no more, that the child would never be able to run properly until she had another child. She had heard Michael had a bad reputation, and was frightened by what he'd said. That very week the child took ill and, 17 weeks later, died. On a separate occasion, her servant, Alice Beere, refused to lend a hatchet to Peter Trevisard, and he sarcastically said that he'd do a good turn for her too. Shortly afterwards she sickened and died. Alice Butler also linked the death of her husband and another child to this episode.

William Cozen, a sailor living at Hardnesse, recalled having a dispute with Michael early in 1600, and a few months later his daughter-in-law Joyce William was stricken with an inexplicable malady in which her neck shrank down and her chin was brought down to her chest, where it remained. Also, when his wife Johan was on her deathbed she told him to keep Alice away from her grave, beating her if necessary.

Christian Webber of Hardnesse leased Michael a property there for an annual rent of 26s 8d, but he only gave her 6s and 8d. She met Alice and demanded the balance of 20s, but Alice pronounced that it would be worse for her. Shortly afterwards, Christian's neighbour Isabel Tozar saw Alice casting water on Christian's stairs, and told her about it. Christian was too afraid to use the stairs for some time, until Alice herself used them and within an hour fell ill, eventually losing parts of her fingers and toes.

Christopher Honywell, a lad of about 13, said that at Whitsuntide 1601 he had been with Peter at Hardnesse where fishermen hung their nets to dry. Peter had pushed his father's boat out into the water and told it to go, unmanned, to the new quay and fetch up between two lighters. Christopher had then gone with Peter to the new quay, an estimated distance of some two arrow shots, and there they found the boat squeezed into the narrow space between two berthed lighters.

On Wednesday January 20th, 1601 (1602), Johan Davye of Hardnesse described how her husband George had once had an argument with Michael, and that within a week her young child had leaped from her arms into the fire and was badly hurt. Michael was at Mr Lovett's house in Hardnesse, playing cards when somebody arrived and broke the news about the accident (she took pains to point out that he was gambling when pious folks would be at their evening prayers). Michael announced that he could help the child if he wanted to, and his companions promptly urged him to do so, but he said he'd never help the Davyes family, and added that he could do them harm to the sum of 20 nobles, if he wished. The next week George was severely wounded in a shooting accident.

On Saturday March 13th, 1601 (1602), John Venman, a Kingswear merchant, reported that he was visiting Mother Blachford at Bridgetown, Totnes, seeking a cure for a sick child of his, when she told him that the child was ill because Alice had bewitched it. The old woman said that Alice had been to his house on the morning the child took ill, adding that she had been carrying a letter. Upon his return home, John's daughter confirmed the story saying Alice had arrived with a letter for his wife. However, John's wife had been out of the house at the time, and their daughter had refused to accept the letter herself because she was afraid of Alice, having heard she was a witch. John added that so far as he knew, Alice had made no attempt to deliver the letter again.

On Wednesday April 7th, 1602, John Galsworthie of Hardnesse said that in or around 1597 his wife asked Alice to pay some money she owed. Alice said she prayed God would not allow her to prosper either in health or wealth. John said his wife did not enjoy good health after that, and died at Christmas 1600. He himself had been taken lame shortly after Alice's malediction, and remained on crutches for a year. Also, within six weeks of her outburst, their gravid sow's piglets died inside her.

It seems as though almost every calamity in the community was being blamed on the Trevisards. Apart from their habit of ill-wishing people and predicting doom and gloom (both perhaps the reactions of proud family facing a mounting vendetta against them), there are a couple of incidents that are notable above and beyond the ordinary spiteful remarks spoken in the heat of the moment.

the weird and wondrous

The first that caught my eye was the story about Alice throwing a liquid onto Christian Webber's stairs — was this a prank intended to make them slippery and induce a fall, or had Alice actually brewed up some sort of magical potion and sprinkled it around like unholy water? If we assume the latter, we may further speculate that the potion contained toxic ingredients that ate away at her fingers. But then why where her toes affected? Perhaps she spilled a little, or walked barefoot on the steps.

The other weird incident is the feat of young Peter and the boat. If we rule out the possibility of an accomplice hidden aboard, it seems that the only rational explanation is Christopher Honywell was lying. But it's such a bizarre story to make up — surely a teenager would have come up with something more exciting. Maybe Peter was just a gifted child with a remarkable intuitive ability to sense how the currents were flowing (a similarly acute knowledge of the wind may have enabled his father to foresee what would happen to the mayor's timber store). I wonder if either ever understood the strength of the currents of enmity swirling among their neighbours, a contagious hostility that would threaten and perhaps overwhelm them in spate.

In 1736 the law was changed to reflect the judiciary's new stance of no longer officially believing in magical powers. However, anyone purporting to use magical powers could still be prosecuted, a situation that was not repealed until the Fraudulent Mediums Act of 1951. This Act (broadly speaking, and without prejudice) only makes obtaining financial or other reward by intentionally deceiving people with claims of mediumship, clairvoyance, etc (except for pure entertainment) an offence; and this has been invoked to occasionally secure convictions. Nowadays, Human Rights legislation and Britain's obligations to uphold religious freedom and condemn religious discrimination, both positively enshrine the right of explorers of the Wiccan path to enjoy a legal freedom to pursue their practises (respecting, of course, the rights of others).

It is only in these more enlightened times, therefore, that we may see a variety of cathartic superstitions springing up. One such has been introduced to Woodlands Leisure Park, which we have already mentioned as occupying land formerly belonging to Oldstone Manor at Blackawton, including the woodland pond where Laura's ghost has been reported. The park's 2005 advertising brochure refers to a charming Halloween practice in which children light candles, each representing a wish, and place them on the haunted pond so they float out into the night. It is easy to imagine the quivering little living flames lit with the spirit of childhood's dearest dreams — a flotilla of wholesome hopes brightening the night.

the fear of God

There is a Biblical proverb that suggests fear of God is the beginning of wisdom;[11] and although many view rule by terror (or the fear of terror) as deeply suspect, like most time-honoured sayings it does contain an element of truth. Fear compels us to contrast ourselves against the source of the threat, and this act of separating ourselves from what we fear instils discrimination. We have already tasted the fear of witchcraft that swept through the country, now we may see how terrible God can be.

Henry Burton, an ardent Puritan, recorded what happened in Dartmouth on May Day 1634, and how those events culminated in a man's death: a death that Burton clearly regarded as divine intervention and retribution — literally an act of God.

Although many urban centres such as London and Bristol had already dispensed with their traditional maypoles, in the countryside the annual return of vegetation to full life was such a powerful event that celebrations continued in spite of the condemnation of evangelical Protestants. Indeed, while the poet Robert Herrick was vicar at Dean Prior (little more than a dozen miles to the northwest of Dartmouth) in the 1630s, he wrote a strong defence of the "harmlesse follie" of this seasonal festivity. His *Corinna's Going A-Maying* describes how the rural population streamed into the country and returned to garland every home with greenery and blossoming branches:

> *Come, my Corinna, come; and, comming, marke*
> *How each field turns a street, each street a Parke*
> *Made green, and trimm'd with trees; see how*
> *Devotion gives each House a Bough,*

It is possible that the festivities in the villages and hamlets around Dartmouth saw festivities on this scale, but it is perhaps unlikely that the town itself festooned itself so gaily. But Burton's tale, which was designed to end the custom, has ironically preserved a glimpse of Dartmouth's local celebration. His story is briefly stated, and begins before dawn on the morning of May Day when a group of young men trooped out of the town to cut down a tree for the maypole (although the text does not record it, a favoured tree for this purpose was birch). Their procession was high-spirited and their merriment was accompanied by the music of trumpet and drum. Burton insisted that this noise so alarmed the neighbourhood that some people believed an invasion was underway.

With the tree brought home and set up, the festivities began in earnest. Unfortunately we are not privy to what part the local women took in the proceedings, but at least some of the men took to drinking toasts around the maypole and, as Burton notes, actually to the maypole itself. With a neat but rather sarcastic touch of wit he adds that their drinking continued until they were no longer able to stand as steady as the pole they'd erected.

---

[11] First recorded in Psalms 111:10 by David c. 1,000 BCE, but the saying is more famously echoed by his son Solomon in Proverbs 9:10.

With the men falling down drunk, the authorities deemed it safe and prudent to disperse the revellers and, by order of the Mayor and Justice, the ringleaders were accused of disorderly conduct and bound over to the Sessions. However, the Archbishop's Vicar-General was inclined to dismiss the charges and, according to Burton at least, God took such a dim view of the leniency of the court that he took the matter into his own hands: one of those accused, whom Burton condemned as a libertine and scornful of authority, promptly "fell into a Consumption, whereof he shortly after died."

God was not, however, content with this show of divine authority against this one individual. According to Burton, although the May Day revelry was not actually on a Sunday (the 1st of May was a Thursday), the fact it took place and the maypole set up at *all*, was enough to profane all the Sundays in the rest of the year. He said succinctly "it was sufficient to provoke God to send plagues and judgements among men." So, all the ills that afflicted the population that year were due to the wrath of God who had decided to teach his merry-making creations a lesson. Burton wrote it all down[12] to ensure people should not forget it, and this tale does indeed serve as a warning to us all.

nature spirits

The previous chapter detailed what happened when Maia visited the site of the principal Oldstone haunting; now we can look more closely at her other experiences at the lower pond. As she approached it, she sensed a sort of misty white column of spiritual energy flowing upwards out of the water.

"The column was two metres wide, coming from way deep in the earth heart within the pond, and rising up to the sky out of sight. It was roaring quietly but had no movement exactly. It had power but was not showing it through movement."

It was one of the largest columns she has seen, but it was not as active as some others: "The activity within them varies, sometimes still and sometimes swirling within them." She added: "I see these in all sorts of places, and I call them Old Energy as that is what I feel they are. They appear to me as light sources from deep in the earth. I think it is water related and it is like a beacon."

Maia also felt the presence of nature spirits residing there. She is familiar with spirits of the traditional elements — earth, water, air, and fire — and told me "The most common ones are small light balls that link to flowers and small plants, similar ones are linked to trees, only bigger.

"The ones I saw in Woodland Park were light balls about ping pong ball size.[13] They glow and move and tinkle, I think they are tree spirits / tree faeries (the ones I see

---

[12] Henry Burton 1641, *A Divine Tragedie Lately Acted*, London, privately printed.

[13] An official table tennis ball measures 40mm (approximately 1.5 inches).

associated with flowers are much smaller). They were all around the edges of the pool and in the green of the trees and plants. There were thirty, maybe more. They moved independently to each other in all directions at about one metre off the ground on average, going high and low in their dancing.

"They did not mind the rain, I asked.

"These beings love anything to do with creation. Lovemaking attracts them... I always see them and hear the tinkle in green clean places. I like them. What are they? Beings of our Earth I believe. Alternate life forms that coexist with us."

Perhaps another sighting of one of these entities occurred in the winter of 1983-1984. The bridge at the head of Old Mill Creek carries the small road connecting Townstal, Dartmouth, with the hamlet of Bruckton in the civil parish of Dittisham. Just to the west of this bridge the road is flanked with woodland, and it was here that a couple of young men rested awhile beneath the sheltering boughs of a large conifer.

To their astonishment a luminous orb about the size of an apple drifted down above their heads. This ball of 'living light' hovered at eye level in front of them for a while before darting away to one side in a straight, horizontal line. Although interpreted as a visitation from a spiritual being, there are features in this tale of the light sphere that are also reminiscent of UFOs, which have been said to emit small probes for reconnaissance.

Another aspect of the world of nature spirits, maintains that these spirits may be able to take on the shape of animals, or perhaps that the behaviour of ordinary animals can be influenced by these spirits. Many familiar superstitions — such as the ones about the lucky black cat that crosses your path, or the counting rhyme that predicts your future based on the number of magpies you see — are all testimony to the idea that somehow everything in life is linked by an invisible yet meaningful matrix of spirituality.

In 1999, from July to September, Kevin Pyne used to pick up his wife Lyzie from the local hospital and spend time together enjoying the summer weather boating on the river they both dearly loved. And every time they went out they were followed by two dolphins (or 'angels of the sea' as Kevin poetically calls them) a rare treat indeed. She was seriously ill at the time, in fact terminally so, and Kevin told me about the dolphins: "The night she died they went, and they were never seen again."

His friends eventually persuaded him to once again take an interest in the water sports the couple had so often enjoyed together, and on the second anniversary of her death he relented and went to Newquay to watch the County Gigs Championships. One race was particularly poignant for Kevin because Lyzie had often been a part of the crew that were competing. During that race, and to his astonishment and the very great surprise of the crew she used to row with, their boat was accompanied by two dolphins.

Kevin is a big-hearted man with a profound love of the Dart, and a view of life that recognises the value of the fleeting moment and yet is as timeless and firm as the bedrock of his beloved county of Devon. Small wonder then that he has gained a reputation as a poet, and he is willing to accept that there may be things in this quiet corner of the country that are not commonly seen. In the preface of his first book of poetry dedicated to his wife he conjures the old mariners' tales of mermaids — or 'merry maids' as he prefers to call them — and who are we to gainsay his idea that her spirit may have taken on the form of those mythic beings of the sea she loved so dearly?[14]

spirit of tHe DARt

In the Bronze Age and for millennia thereafter, rivers such as the Dart were the motorways of commerce, and it should be remembered that the river's natural deep-water harbourage was not only the source of Dartmouth's continuing prosperity but is the reason the town exists at all. A famous traditional verse is often quoted in celebration of the memorable loveliness of the place:

> River Dart! River Dart!
> Every year thou claim'st a heart!

The Dart flows through some of the most glorious scenery in Devon, and the river's merging with the sea at Dartmouth is so picturesque that every year it captivates many a heart with its beauty. But legends from the bleaker vistas upstream suggest an older and more sinister interpretation, and remind us of the Dart's ancient reputation as 'the Dangerous River'. The couplet's personification of the river as a being with a taste for human flesh echoes the Celtic religion of pantheism in which everything is spiritually alive and has its own individual spirit: animals, trees, rocks, valleys and rivers, all have a spirit that can communicate with us, and we with them.

The spirit of the Dart has been heard many times through the centuries calling alluringly, almost hypnotically, for its next victim. The voice is described as deep yet feminine, and howling (even when the weather is calm). Although as silent as a shadow, the spirit of the Dart described in the following tale offers a very graphic idea of how it can manifest. A version of this has been published on the Internet under the title The River Ghost,[15] but it does not involve any ordinary sort of ghost. Rather, this manifestation seems to belong to a class of entity known as a 'genius loci', or spirit of a place.

The events occurred one night in September 1993 when canoeist Phil Sheardown and his partner took to the river to experience what was billed to be the highest tidal rise

---

[14] Kevin Pyne 2004, *Further up the River*, Dartmouth, Richard Webb.

[15] Phil Sheardown 2001, *The River Ghost*, http://www.ukriversguidebook.co.uk/dartghoststory.htm .

of the 20th century. The evening was clear and fine as they set out to paddle downstream from Totnes Plain in a big canoe named *Dinosaur*. The autumn twilight deepened rapidly and soon they were steering by starlight, using the Plough and Polestar to keep their bearings.

Having become accustomed to the gloom, they suddenly spotted danger ahead: a white mist stretched across the river like a wall fully three yards (2.7m) high. They realised that if they were enveloped in its whiteout while caught in the surging current of this once-in-a-lifetime megatide, they could not hope to avoid the river's numerous hazards.

In Phil's own words: "It was on the level glimmering bank of starlit mist ahead that the haunting began. First a bubble of mist formed like an igloo on the top of the bank of it across the river. When I looked back again from the stars the igloo had swelled and extended into a rising column of twisting mist rearing up, silent, the thickness of a lighthouse, rearing and curving like a towering snake, impossible to look away. Then to unbelief, a misty head the size of a bus and trailing long misty tassels, formed on top of the column. Skin and hair crawled seething up and down backs of arms legs and neck in absolute bone primitive ghost fear. It saw us, it knew we were there. The impulse to panic, backwater, turn the canoe and flee was incredible. The starlit monster head turned nodding, tracking our approach and no help for it but to keep steady and be swept directly underneath. It was alive, part of the river out and about in its natural habitat, we the intruders. Sure, it was a wraith, hungry, out hunting for fresh human anguish to feed upon, anguish produced in fear panic and lethal lingering accident. As we neared it I waited for something unimaginable to happen, a hole in the water, a wet muddy giant hand reaching up from below for us, the shock and icy vice of deep cold water. No one would know, and we'd be dead."

Although the mist was dense it was not as extensive as it appeared, but as they surged through it at about three knots (1.5m/s), they passed the quarter-ton (0.25t) channel buoy at Ham Reach and realised what a narrow escape they had had. If they had backwatered in an attempt to avoid the shrouding mist they would have struck the buoy sideways and been pitched into the merciless flood.

They terminated their adventure at the next safe landing place, but the following day they received a further shock. An experienced yachtsman visiting Dartmouth had drowned as he returned in a dinghy to his yacht moored off Warfleet Creek. The time of his accident coincided uncannily with their own nearly disastrous encounter with the river ghost.

Such is Phil's love of our waterways that he set up his own company Canoe Adventures in 1999, offering beginners and experienced canoeists alike the opportunity to explore the wonders of our natural waterways; he often tells his tale to guest-crews in his canoes, but rarely after dark.

SPRING-HEELED JACK

A well-known spirit, or goblin perhaps, is Spring-heeled Jack whose roving antics, and acrobatic prowess achieved considerable fame in late Victorian London — and Dartmouth had its own mischievous and equally invisible sprite that was given the same nickname. William Pengelly (writing in the same article as the white rabbit, above) interviewed a seventy-year old gardener born in Dittisham who had lived in Dartmouth or Kingswear for the past forty years, and who knew a "good many people" that had experience of Spring-heeled Jack in Dartmouth.

The unnamed gardener went on to describe how Jack created a disturbance at night by loudly "rattling his chain" while taking long leaps and bounds, even up onto the rooftops. What could possibly chain such a free spirit to the physical plane is unknown but it seems certain that this was no ordinary ghost.

We have already noted that the Weeke / Gallant's Bower area is renowned for spectral horses and headless riders, producing some of Dartmouth's most terrifying supernatural spectacles. When I told Philip Law about these he told me "it made the hairs on my back stand up". And this bizarre clustering of strange tales seems to suggest they share a common origin. Although it is not yet possible to determine their source, this gathering of exceptionally gruesome phenomena does seem to indicate the presence of something much more unnatural and mysterious than simple ghosts.

Perhaps a clue to this sinister reputation was given to me by a local man who preferred to remain anonymous. He told me that in the mid 1950s the then manageress of the Royal Castle Hotel, Mrs Powell, had an interest in spiritualism and was herself somewhat 'fey'. One day she announced the hotel's famous ghostly coach was going to call, and that it would bring passengers and it probably wouldn't call again. Shortly afterwards the sounds of the horses and carriage were heard in the hotel but this time their visit had a grisly aftermath. The next morning news began to spread of a tragedy that had taken place in one of the houses along Weeke Hill — Mr Howard Koppenhagen, a director of the Dartmouth Pottery at Warfleet, had slain his wife, young daughter and the family dog and then turned the gun on himself.

Rumour swiftly linked Mrs Powell's prediction with this dreadful event, and the coachman assumed the character of Death himself. Of course, in contradiction to the prophecy, the coach has been heard to return since then, and the idea that its arrival was in any way connected with the deaths is purely conjectural. In fact, this story has many of the hallmarks of an urban legend whose details were conflated from a number of sources. Although my informant's memory is sound enough, he moved to the town and heard the story a couple of years after the events were said to have occurred — ample time in which the tale could have evolved from what may have been nothing more than an unfortunate melding of chance comments and coincidence.

THE GREEN MAN

*The Green Man at
St Saviour's, Dartmouth
(see front endpapers).*

*The Green Man at
St George's, Dittisham.*

Another spirit that is supposed to be a relic of our pagan past is preserved in the church of St Saviour, Dartmouth: it is a little carved image of the Green Man on the wooden Rood Screen. As is usual, only his head is depicted but he is unmistakable as large leaves sprout from his mouth. The screen was constructed in 1496, some 200 years after the site was consecrated, and this date places the effigy at the extreme end of the period in which almost all his British compatriots were erected: 1300 to 1500.[16]

I located two stone examples of the Green Man in the immediate area — one dates from 1328 to 1333 when the formerly Norman church in Dittisham (St George) was rebuilt: he gazes down from the eastern edge of the ceiling of the south porch. The other is situated on the capital of the column at the northwestern end of the nave of the church of St Michael, at Blackawton, which is of 15th century date.

There was, it seems, no apparent pattern governing the positioning of these remarkable effigies, but they clearly remained an integral element in local ecclesiastic architecture for more than a hundred and fifty years. This leafy emblem, which seemingly represents 'the spirit of plants', is particularly common in Devon's churches, but it is also found in many parts of western Europe as well as the Middle East and even India. In view of the importance this symbol once enjoyed, it seems incredible that we do not know exactly what these faces represent.

The generic term 'Green Man' is modern and was coined in 1939 by Lady Ragland of the Folklore Society, with reference to a widespread British pub sign depicting a forester. Many researchers have linked him with the Jack in the Green famed in

---

[16] Kathleen Basford 1978, *The Green Man*, Cambridge, D S Brewer.

The Green Man at
St Michael's, Blackawton.

Mayday revels, and also with the Oak King, but this theory has been brought into question and current thinking doubts that a pagan god could have infiltrated the body of the church. The tide of scholarly opinion now proposes that medieval Christianity employed the image to depict mankind's lowly state of natural ignorance, against which it could contrast the exalted state of spiritual perfection embodied in the ubiquitous figures of its saints (remember, the Reformation had not yet swept away such 'graven images').

The Green Man powerfully personifies the regenerative quality of vegetation that, although apparently perishing each autumn, is renewed or reborn each spring. So, despite the hypothetical original Christian intention, this ancient and widespread symbol could easily have become an honoured emblem for members of the congregation with an affinity for indigenous ideas of the divine. Either way, Christian or pagan, the Green Man is assured of an enduring and even fond place in the annual celebration of eternal resurrection in nature (and, by extension, of all mortal beings).

Incidentally, the name of the greatest Christian festival of Easter derives (if Bede is to be believed) from a Teutonic goddess named Eostre who gave her name to the spring season of new beginnings; her name is actually linked with a family of Indo-European goddesses of the dawn such as the Roman Aurora, Greek Eos, and Indian Ushas.[17] While we're on the subject of death and rebirth, the following quotation regarding local burial practices is from a bound manuscript entitled *St Saviours Church Dartmouth* written around the end of the 19th century by E H Back,[18] and kindly loaned to me by Walter Parr-Ferris.

"Yew trees also with their dense head of sombre foliage spreading their branches like a pall against the brighter tints of the elms also graced the yard as was customary in the early age, the wood being used for bows and the branches for superstitious uses, mourners usually carrying the latter in solemn procession & depositing them in the grave under the bodies of their friends; their idea being that the branches thus out from the tree which would shoot forth again in the coming spring were emblematical of the Resurrection of the body, as by reason of their perpetually verding they were of the immortality of the soul."

---

[17] Ronald Hutton 1996, *The Stations of the Sun*, Oxford, Oxford University Press.
[18] Believed to be the architect and borough surveyor Edwin Herbert Back, born 1843, who was living with his family in Victoria Street, Dartmouth, at the time of the 1901 Census.

THE DARK AND THE LIGHT

Along the south bank of Old Mill Creek (to the north of Dartmouth town centre) lies Sandquay Wood. It is a sylvan haven where a fresh-water stream sings beneath an ancient stone bridge, and woodpeckers tenant the living pillars of this natural temple whose vault is of the finest green lattice. But one midsummer's night this tranquil beauty spot showed its sinister side.

It was in 1981 that a courting couple returning to town chose a short-cut along a narrow footpath beside the Creek. Entering a small glade not far from Boone's Quay the young woman grew nervous, complaining of insistent déjà-vu. It seemed as if fragments of a long-forgotten dream were being mirrored by her surroundings. Unfortunately the dream had the hallmarks of a nightmare.

For an instant they shared a vision that turned their amble home to stumbling flight. Clearly visible in the moonlight, a squat, black-robed figure stood beside a tree five or six yards (c. 5m) away. Despite the fact that the being was barely a yard (0.9m) tall, it radiated all the physical strength of a powerful and malevolent bear.

It was no trick of the light, they saw it from different angles; neither was it a child, for it vanished silently and in the twinkling of an eye. It actually seemed as if a portal to the underworld had suddenly yawned before them, a glimpse of living oblivion.

They each instinctively hastened away homeward and only when they were well clear of the haunted glade did they break their silence and confirm the details of the experience to each other.

Remarkably, that wasn't the end of their adventure. A feminine figure, mist white and full of grace accompanied them until they were nearly out of the wood. Her presence was awe-inspiring but definitely not numbingly evil like their earlier dark companion, indeed it seemed as though she was safeguarding them on their journey home.

This contrast between the brutal masculine embodiment of savagery, and the ethereal and transcendental feminine assurance of protection, is a recurring theme in folklore. Those who meet the former but fail to be awarded intervention by the latter may find themselves in a seriously unpleasant situation. In fact, the lover's nocturnal tryst could all too easily have ended in tragedy along the occasionally precipitous, slippery, root-tangled path that winds like a snake above the lapping waters of Old Mill Creek.

Less than a mile away (around 1 km) there was a sighting of something utterly anomalous that might, perhaps, be related to the darker half of that pair of opposed spirits. In or around 1998 at about 9:30 one morning, Anthony Hemmings went with a friend to visit a mutual friend living in the middle of a block of flats at Windsor Road, Townstal. The resident was in the kitchen, with his back towards the others who were seated in the adjoining lounge.

Without warning, something black came through a wall, sped across the room in
a straight line between the friends and out towards the back of the flat, roughly level
with the top of the hill there. Anthony told me "It seemed to emerge from the wall,
through the cupboards; and the door was shut and it just went straight through...
I jumped up straight away and opened the door, and searched all the rooms and
couldn't see anything." He added it was like "looking at a [thin, black] bin liner
but it was almost transparent".

The cupboards were about 3 foot 6 inches (1m) high, and 'it' was very slightly shorter;
it had no definite head or shape, but was a little more than a foot (0.35m) in width
and depth. The shocking sighting lasted for just a few seconds. They immediately told
their host what they had seen, but found no explanation for this extraordinary event.

To balance this modern story, I can't help but wonder whether the traditional tale
of the 'white lady of Black Gate' might also have been another remnant of a similar
spiritual pair. Black Gate was the name of the once green and pleasant valley through
which the broad, straight course of College Way now descends from Townstal toward
the river at Dartmouth. Her spirit used to be seen wandering along a footpath beside
the stream, and her aura of friendliness was legendary.

*The Butterwalk, Dartmouth
(see pages 23,28,102).*

CHAPTER FOUR

from aliens to king arthur

N THIS CHAPTER WE SHALL EXPLORE SOME WEIRD AND WONDERFUL TALES THAT ARE NOT ABOUT GHOSTS OR SPIRITS, BUT TELL OF OTHER ODDITIES INCLUDING FLESH AND BLOOD CREATURES SUCH AS ALIENS, GIANTS AND MONSTERS; OFFER INSIGHTS INTO ALL MANNER OF EARTH ENERGIES SUCH AS LEY LINES; AND EVEN INCLUDE PHENOMENA SUCH AS BIZARRE COINCIDENCES, AND SPONTANEOUS COMBUSTION.

We shall also consider prehistoric astronomical alignments. However, the author's identification of a giant winter constellation in which the stars Sirius, Rigel, Procyon and Aldebaran form a lamp - Lucerna - and a planet visiting Gemini provides the flame of illumination, is not explored. Lucerna's similarity to the South Hams Star (page 107) seems too superficial, despite the river Gara flowing through the landscape like the Milky Way through the heavens (mapped from the perspective of a supine stargazer), to warrant more than a passing mention here.

Some people feel that many of the diverse anomalies scattered through the pages of this book are actually linked, and that splitting them into chapters gives the wrong impression. I confess some sympathy with this view, but feel that for ease of reference the chapters are helpful, and I have tried not to be too arbitrary in my allocation. But I have, for instance, separated witchcraft and ley lines even though some modern witches use earth energies to 'power up', and I admit this partition is for the sake of convenience only.

I have also divided spirits and UFOs although, again, I recognise there are connections between them. Where our forefathers may have spoken of angels or fiery dragons soaring across the sky, of corpse candles or even of 'living lights', we now talk about UFOs. It seems that the names change but the events continue unaltered. So, without further preamble, it is high time to go boldly on a voyage into the heavens.

Blackdown Rings hillfort (see pages 64, 65, 107, 108).

UNIDENTIFIED FLYING OBJECTS

On Sunday December 11th, 1881, people in Dartmouth Harbour saw two bright, inexplicable lights in the sky, and were sufficiently concerned to report the event to the press.[1] It is fortunate that, despite the perennial fear of ridicule, people still have the courage of their convictions, and continue to publicise their experiences in the hope of discovering the answer to their nagging questions: What on earth was it? And was it from earth at all?

Alan Neal was a child when in 1947 or perhaps 1946 he was on a caravan holiday with his family at Stoke Fleming. On one memorable ramble through the countryside, they sat down for a rest at Venn Cross, a half-an-hour stroll to the north of the village. Alan told me he "Looked up and saw something that looked like a silver pencil, high up, making a humming noise." He added "There was nothing like that flying at that time, it was quite unusual. It stayed hovering above us, then shot off out over the sea. It shot off too quickly for a dirigible."

There was a spate of UFO sightings in the Southwest in 1978. This 'flap' (to use the ufologists' jargon) provided multiple sightings from Dartmoor, Exeter, Tiverton, and Bovey Tracy as well as Dartmouth.

On Monday October 16th, 1978, Charlie Pitts and his 13-year-old daughter reported seeing several UFOs about 8pm. They were at Townstal's industrial estate when they saw a silver ball hovering in the sky in the direction of Dittisham. It seemed to be pulsating and moved in a smooth line towards Slapton. They saw a similar object the following evening.

Spherical UFO over the BRNC.

Later that month Michael Appleton and Collin Cozens reported to the local paper[2] that they had seen red and white lights flashing in the evening sky, moving towards the Britannia Royal Naval College (BRNC).

It is likely that the following incident occurred in that remarkable year but the witness can only affirm that it was between 1977 and 1979. One fine evening between July and September, at 7pm, the witness was in Kingswear. There wasn't a cloud in the sky. Gazing across the water towards Dartmouth he noticed a bright light hovering above the clock tower at the BRNC. He thought little of it initially, presuming it to be something quite ordinary, but after a couple of hours had passed he realised that there was something unusual going on.

---

[1] Charles Fort 1923, *New Lands*, New York, Boni and Liveright.

[2] *Dartmouth Chronicle*, 3 November 1978.

With his curiosity aroused, he brought a pocket telescope to bear on the object and observed it carefully. From his position, the UFO was to the north-northwest, and at an elevation of about 15 degrees. The drawing is based on the detailed description he gave me: the central area of the sphere was pure white, and the rest of the orb constantly changed hue. The streamers were shiny like tinsel.

Dartmouth boatman Kevin Pyne and deckhand Eddie Preece were manning the Lower Ferry one February night in 1988 or 1989 when early in one clear, cold evening they saw a large delta-winged object fly into view at a very low altitude from the Warfleet area. It had a cluster or cross of white lights on its otherwise matt blue-black underside, and a wingspan of at least 35m.

Kevin told me "It was a quiet evening at the bottom of the tide. And we saw this huge black shape come over Warfleet Creek, bank, and fly up the river and fly over us and then fly past us and bank and go over the old Golf Club."

Eddie said they had a good view of it before it veered over Hillhead and disappeared towards Torquay, and estimated its speed at more than 300 knots (555 km/hr). Eddie, who had spent fifteen years in the Navy and was born in Dartmouth, was familiar with early delta-winged aircraft such as the Vulcan, but described this craft as being more like an equilateral triangle, adding "the strangest thing about it was it was completely silent."

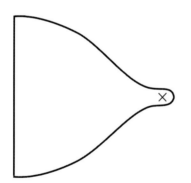

When Kevin arrived home he mentioned it to his wife Lyzie, saying "You'll never guess what I've seen tonight."

"Yep," she replied. "A spaceship, I was taking the washing in — I saw it go by." She had seen it fly over the hill at Kingswear; and Eddie told me another witness, a friend's son, had watched it from his bedroom window.

Delta-winged UFO over the Dart.

Kevin, who was in his late 30s when he had this encounter, had spent years in the Air Training Corps and remains convinced this was no conventional aircraft, particularly because of the absence of any noise — something even the latest 'stealth' aircraft aren't even close to achieving. Triangular craft with this and other similarly 'impossible' characteristics have been seen countless times, particularly in the late 1980s and 1990s. Some such sightings have been debunked as military, hi-tech stealth planes from the United States (many ufologists cite the Aurora project as the tip of a covert iceberg), but many reliable witnesses such as Kevin and Eddie report aspects of the craft's behaviour that are still the stuff of aviators' dreams.

The *Sunday Independent* of October 10th, 1982, had a two-page story of a UFO photographed in May from Dartmouth looking across the harbour towards the fields of Kingswear. The landscape photograph shows a slightly blurred object that lacks symmetry, but conventional explanations are not readily forthcoming. The UFO is shaped rather like a boater type of straw hat, which made me wonder whether somebody had tossed something like a Frisbee into the air. However, anybody throwing such an item would also have been clearly visible in the photograph. The shape could also have been quickly dismissed as a lenticulate cloud except that these usually lie flat, whereas this object is tilted at an angle of some 20 degrees.

More recently still, a silver disc-shaped object was seen to hover and move slowly across the heavens around 9:20 on the evening of Tuesday July 23rd, 1996.[3]

UNIDENTIFIED fiery objects

It is often said that UFO reports are mostly misinterpretations of natural phenomena, and although I have not been able to interview the witnesses of the following incident myself, I wonder whether this 'flying saucer' sighting at Kingswear might be a case in point.

The report made front page news in a local newspaper[4] in December 1950, and concerned two dairy workers who were in the fields of Nethway Farm at around 6am on Wednesday 13th. Roger Perkins (a young man of 18 years) and Leslie Chester (who was middle aged) saw a bright light in the cloudless, pre-dawn sky: it was streaking towards them across the sea from the northeast leaving a trail of sparks in its wake.

Mr Perkins estimated its speed at around 300 miles per hour (480 km/hr) and its height at between 2,000 and 3,000 feet (approximately 600m to 900m). It should be noted that this sighting was shortly after the end of the Second World War, when many people on the south coast had learned to calculate the details of enemy aircraft. As it reached the farm the brilliance suddenly faded, the object split into two, and promptly disappeared.

Although Mr Perkins went on to say that the object was not a shooting star, I wonder whether it was actually an uncommonly large meteor known as a fireball. These relatively rare natural objects have been noted to fragment as they plunge through the atmosphere, sometimes falling at such a low angle they appear to fly in a horizontal line. Certainly fireballs don't resemble ordinary shooting stars, and for most people seeing one is a once in a lifetime experience (I saw a fragmenting meteor over Kingsteignton in the early 1970s, which not only had an almost level flightpath but burned with a bright emerald green colour).

---

[3] Michael Joyce 2001, *Essex UFO Research Group Reported Sightings*, http://www.jufo.freeserve.co.uk/page34.html .

[4] *Herald Express*, 13 December 1950.

The newspaper reported the object as a flying saucer even though the printed description doesn't warrant that particular phrase (which had been coined just four years earlier in 1946), because there had been a spate of similar sightings in South Devon beginning in October that year — one of which did mention a disc.[5] Reports of balls of fire flying through the skies of the Southwest continued for several years afterwards, and therein lies the puzzle: the Kingswear sighting could easily be dismissed as a meteor (hastily pigeonholed according to the fashion of the day), but it would be impossible for a series of fireballs to cluster over this area over such a period. So, if they can't all be meteors, what were they? These flying objects remain for now unidentified.

A more modern sighting occurred on a clear evening in June or July 1998. James Thomas was working on the Passenger Ferry when he and a passenger saw an object in the sky that he has been unable to identify. It was a light, shining from the direction of Gallants Bower but well above the hill — at first it was "red, it went yellowish, then burning white with sparks breaking off it until it vaporised."

He watched it for between five and ten minutes, and all the while it was "hanging in the air." He added "it was moving directly for us as it was getting bigger, but it was still a long way off."

A normal meteor would have disintegrated in just a few seconds, and it is hard to imagine even a large meteorite or fireball lasting so long, even if it were heading directly toward you. Another natural interpretation seemed plausible, so I asked James whether it could possibly have been a flare (which are sometimes suspended from a little parachute to keep them aloft). He firmly denied this interpretation however, saying "I know the difference — it was not a flare." Taking him at his word, this too remains an unidentified aerial object.

supernatural force field

We are familiar with the idea of alien spacecraft having protective force fields around them, and a witch or wizard's magic circle is also a wall of energy insulating them from psychic interference, but the following uncanny tale is in a class of its own. One night around 1970 a local man was out walking his dog: they had just rounded the corner into Duke Street from 'the Boatfloat' (The Quay), and were heading toward the ancient colonnade when they bumped up against an invisible barrier. Shocked but undaunted the man crossed the road and tried to walk past it there, but his efforts were in vain. The force field extended right across the road.

With commendable presence of mind he held out his hand and actually touched the barrier, which felt as solid as a wall, and stretched higher than he could reach.

[5] A W Bearne 1968, *Flying Saucers over the West*, privately printed.

Alarmed, he turned in his tracks and tried a different way home. The route he chose was the one around behind the Butterwalk buildings, but the very same obstacle prevented him from passing (we may note that the Butterwalk was built on land reclaimed from the river, and that this side originally remained open water). Not surprisingly, he promptly despaired of the whole area and took an extensive detour that led him home without further adventure.

Many stories are told elsewhere of dogs and other animals refusing in enter certain rooms or even buildings: places with an eerie atmosphere and a reputation for paranormal activity. Perhaps this force field is an extreme example of this well-known yet little understood effect.

earth energies — the dart's chakras

A tantalising mention in Totnes author Bob Mann's local ghost book,[6] describes a landscape temple in the form of a giant lying along the course of the river Dart. Bob, who is an expert on many aspects of the paranormal in the locality, and was the Folklore Recorder for the Devonshire Association (for the Advancement of Science, Literature and the Arts) from 1994 to 1998, told me he heard of the idea in an article carried in the Dartington Voice, the internal newsletter of the Dartington Hall Trust, in the early 1980s. The original idea had come from Peter Dawkins, an author perhaps best known for his Zoence project, which has been compared to a modern Western system of Feng Shui and promotes a creative union between people and our environment.

Peter answered my enquiry saying he used to lead Earth Mysteries pilgrimages in the locality, and had composed an information paper on the topic. He put me in touch with the Gatekeeper Trust, an educational charity he founded to promote healing through exploring the landscape. Maggi Fielder, editor of *Gatekeeper News* and a local contact for Devon,[7] kindly gave me more details.

"Certain places" she wrote, "have been recognised as 'power centres', rather like acupuncture points on the body, through which the whole person can be healed. Working in groups at these places can have a powerful effect on the body of the planet itself.

"By pilgrimaging to places in the landscape to which you feel drawn, and offering your healing love through meditation, dance, song or whatever way feels right to you, places and communities can be transformed."

---

[6] Bob Mann 1993, *The Ghosts of Totnes*, Exeter, Obelisk Publications.

[7] For current information on Gatekeeper activities in south Devon, phone 01803 849 399 or visit http://www.gatekeeper.org.uk .

The curtain wall, Dartmouth Castle (see page 78).

In the words of Peter Dawkins: "A pilgrim's relationship with the earth, with the landscape, can be a love relationship. The earth in her love for us helps us towards illumination, and we can help her towards hers. That is the hidden purpose of pilgrimage — the so-called redemption of mankind and nature, the raising of all to light, wherein light is the manifestation of love."

The power centres of the Dart's giant figure are envisaged as a chakra system: a series of metaphysical energy hubs:[8]

Dartmouth is situated at the bottom of the spine, the base, or root chakra which, Maggi informed me, relates to the will to live, and the survival instinct — making the town's naval college particularly appropriate.

The next higher chakra, the sacral, engenders the powers of sexual procreation and related emotions, and is situated on the Dart at the Anchor Stone rock (slightly downstream from Dittisham) and reaches upstream as far as Sharpham near Ashprington.

The third chakra of this system, the solar plexus, is situated at Totnes and principally relates to personal power and the energy derived from nourishment, which seems appropriate for an ancient market town.

---

[8] Chakras are associated with the human body, and are aligned vertically through the trunk and head. Since their conception in ancient India, divergent traditions have evolved to satisfy a range of applications. Most Western authorities opt to work with only seven chakras, cherry-picking those that best illustrate their interests.

The heart chakra is pivotal to the entire system and is strongly associated with balance as well as compassion, love, peace, and emotional healing: it is located at Dartington, the internationally renowned centre for arts and crafts.

The throat chakra is concerned with self-expression and ideas of self-worth, and is situated in the area of the Rudolf Steiner school at Hood Manor (near Riverford Bridge).

The 'ajna' chakra is often called the third eye, and relates to the mind's more sophisticated powers, ranging from lucid memory and dreams to psychic insight; it is located at Buckfast Abbey.

The seventh and topmost chakra, the crown, is often visualised as a white lotus blossom with a thousand petals, and refers to spiritual awareness, enlightenment, and holistic wellbeing; it is located on Dartmoor, near Dartmeet.

A glance at a map reveals that although these power centres are roughly aligned, their spacing does not fit the human body shape: the head is almost as large as the torso. Clearly there is an inbuilt warning against taking things too literally. Comparing the meaning of each chakra to the type of human activity at the quoted location is crucial to evaluating the theory but, unfortunately, this task is easily bedevilled by subjective bias. While some people might say the correspondences can only be seen with the eye of faith, others regard them as self-evident.

My researches revealed another traditional role of the bottom chakra: the anal recycling of bodily waste into the environment, which is symbolised by the outpouring of the Dart into the sea. Whichever way you look at it, whereas people living or working in the Dartington complex might bask in the reflected glory of the heart chakra's beauty and vitality, people in Dartmouth might need a lot of persuasion to embrace the idea that their town sits at the giant's backside. Of course, the 'muladhara' chakra is a perfectly honourable one (indeed it is the firm base without which the whole edifice would topple), and much too could be said in honour of the genital chakra to reassure the good folk of Dittisham.

This certainly demonstrates the gulf between the language of mystics and everyday ideas; it seems a competent guide and interpreter may be essential on a pilgrimage such as this.

earth energies — Ley Lines

Alfred Watkins is renowned for coining the term 'ley', and his highly influential book *The Old Straight Track* has been reprinted many times since 1925. He believed leys were prehistoric trackways that, like modern roadways, encouraged settlement along their route and especially at crossroads. Arable farming, introduced in the Neolithic period, meant these settlements created clearings in the primal greenwood (Old English 'leah') resulting in local place-names such as Abbotsleigh, Allaleigh, and Moreleigh.

His theory proposed that the native Britons established a system of signposts or way markers along their key routes. Apart from prominent hills and other natural features such as notches on the skyline, other territorial markers such as long barrows, and even hillforts were, he believed, carefully sited to commemorate the ancient alignments. Many of these natural and archaeological sites are depicted on Ordnance Survey maps, making ley hunting a popular sport of amateur folklorists on rainy Sunday afternoons in the 1960s and 70s, when all things alternative enjoyed a pinnacle of interest.

Watkins strongly advocated excursions into the field as opposed to relying on armchair investigations alone, but what he would have thought of the many modern pilgrims to ley markers who use dowsing or other occult means in an attempt to tune-in to a lost golden age of primeval wisdom, is difficult to say. However, I fancy he was broad-minded and maybe romantic enough to indulge such whims graciously. Which would be all to the good, as his idea of straight tracks (which are not, incidentally, to be confused with Roman roads) has rather fallen out of fashion, being replaced by the dowsers' ideas of wavy 'earth energy lines' that follow serpentine paths around the ley — like the serpents entwined around the caduceus wand of Hermes.

In his exploration of Straight-Sighted Pre-Historic Trackways, Watkins mentions a ley that passes through the Dartmouth Castle / church of St Petrox complex. Following the line to the east this ley crosses the Dart and meets Coleton before continuing along the footpath beside the hedgerow on the ridge that leads down to the sea at Scabbacombe Head (a total distance of almost 2.5 miles (4 km). Following it to the west it runs directly through the Civil War fort of Gallant's Bower, and from there it intersects Weeke Hill at a very narrow angle, before continuing to Riversbridge and Embridge, apparently culminating in a stretch of straight road at Combe Cross, 3.5 miles (5.5 km) from Dartmouth Castle.

Watkins originally included Kingswear Castle in his list of sighting points along this line, but that building is really too far from the straight-and-narrow to be significant in a statistical sense. However, Watkins was unaware that the lost medieval holy site of Trinity Chapel is now believed to be located at the highest point of the hill just west of Coleton Farm, and it would have stood on the line. Ley enthusiasts would be keen to note that the ley hypothesis predicts a significant number of such as-yet undiscovered sites will be found along ley lines.

Prolific Devonshire author Judy Chard discovered a ley line associated with a stream flowing beneath her home at Newton Abbot, and reckoned that it (the ley) continued into Washbourne.[9] The connection between ley lines and underground streams is not

---

[9] Judy Chard 2003, Devon *Stories of the Supernatural*, Newbury, Countryside Books.

particularly well understood, but it has been noted many times since dowsers became interested in leys. In particular, ley markers such as churches and ancient forts are often believed to be sited where one stream crosses over another stream flowing at a different depth.

These leys tend to have a more organic configuration because they follow natural geology and do not adhere rigidly to Alfred Watkins' idea of straight roads. Indeed, the whole idea of a network of roads is often replaced with a grid of power lines, conduits of supernatural energy that can be felt directly by people with a sensitive disposition — or indirectly by using suitable dowsing equipment. Hauntings are often said to be intensified if they occur at a site through which such a ley passes, as if the ghosts can draw upon the energy of the ley, and channel it into their own activities. Likewise, witches are reputed to weave more powerful spells where ley lines cross.

Judy notes that her ley passes through the hilltop churchyard of All Saints at Highweek (Newton Abbot) and approaches Washbourne by way of Berry Pomeroy Castle, which is nationally famous for its enduring and frequent hauntings (sadly, these lie outside the scope of the current book). It takes but a minute with a ruler and map to see these three points cannot be connected with a single straight line.

She projects her ley to the north east, and this part of the line also shows pronounced arcing. From the church of All Saints she says it runs up to Haldon Belvedere, which is also known as Lawrence Castle, and is a well-known landmark tower built in 1788. Although prominent for many miles around, the 18th century date of this building might make it seem a very unlikely marker on an ancient ley, but the remains of a Neolithic settlement have been found on the site. From here her ley continues via Woodbury Salterton to the massive Celtic hill fort of Hembury.

A line connecting the most distantly separated yet clearly identifiable ley markers (i.e. Hembury Hill Fort to the north, and Berry Pomeroy Castle to the south) and projected beyond Washbourne, reaches to within 250m from the large tumulus at Halwell (a key feature — the apex in fact — of the South Hams Star, see facing page). Although an error of 250m over a distance of 60km amounts to a divergence of only about 0.00007 of a degree, I think this suggested alignment is simply coincidence, no matter how tantalisingly close it seems. Many people do, however, believe ley lines form an organised pattern across the whole country, and dedicated attempts have been made to discover whether the system spreads across the entire world, but without unequivocal success to date.

It is worth noting that ordinary maps become misleading over large distances (due to the incongruity of depicting a curved surface such as the Earth on a flat surface), but the South Hams Star, is compact enough to escape the effects of this geometric warping.

the south hams star

This may be one of the most remarkable features in British geomancy —
a five-pointed star or pentagram over 7.5 miles (12 km) wide — or it may
be a prime example of a meaningless coincidence given false credentials
by pure conjecture.

Although I have referred to this geometric shape in a previous publication,[10]
this is the first time details of this tantalising figure have been published. Even
though one of the five 'points' of the star doesn't appear to have a proper
monument marking its position (we shall find a simple solution to this puzzle
in due course), as with most true discoveries, once your attention is drawn to
it, you wonder why nobody noticed it before.

A perfect example of the way we tend to zoom through life without being
aware of the little treasures we pass every moment can be found on the
main road connecting Dartmouth with Totnes, near Halwell. Few motorists

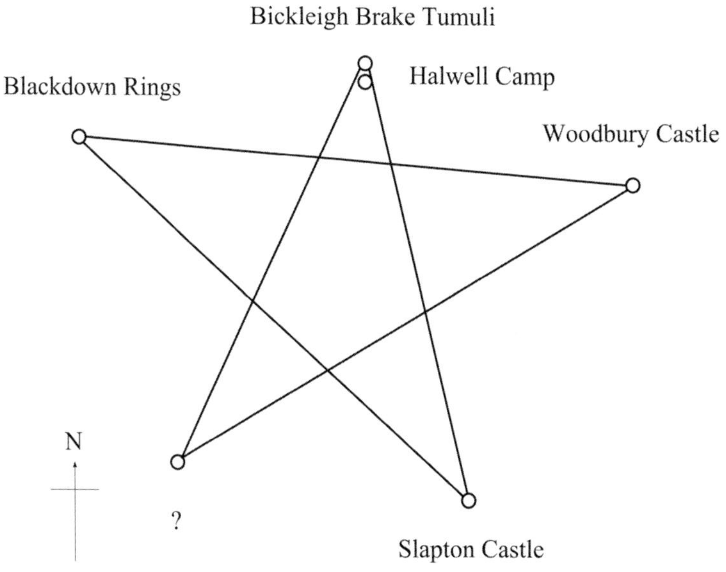

Bickleigh Brake Tumuli

Blackdown Rings

Halwell Camp

Woodbury Castle

N

?

Slapton Castle

The South Hams Star.

[10] Ken Taylor, et al, 2000, *Dreams and Magic*, 126, Bath, Parragon.

following the B3207 just 200 yards (180m) from Halwell Cross realise that they are driving straight through the middle of a prestigious settlement that bustled with life in the Iron Age: Halwell Camp.

Fortunately for those who enjoy stepping out under the open sky and investigating matters for themselves, there is a lay-by at the site of this scheduled ancient monument. The earthen banks of the once fortified Celtic enclosure rise to over six feet (1.8m) in height, and are clearly visible in the field to the north of the road. Yet this is not the earliest surviving structure here: in the fields to the north a meandering row of burial mounds — Bronze Age round barrows — march up to the top of the hill. At least three have been ploughed into obscurity but one, which still retains traces of its original surrounding ditch, is a prominent if slightly overgrown bowl barrow standing six feet (1.8m) tall at Bickleigh Brake.

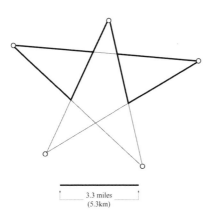

3.3 miles
(5.3km)

Geometry of the Star.

These barrows (denoted "tumuli" on most Ordnance Survey maps), which lie at the head or apex of the star, are Earlier Bronze Age in origin, dating roughly to between 1,800 BCE and 1,400 BCE: these are the earliest known sites on the star.

The uppermost arms of the star are the scheduled hillforts of Woodbury Castle and Blackdown Rings, both of which are thought to be Later Bronze Age to Early Iron Age (roughly 1,000 BCE to 400 BCE). Blackdown Rings actually contains the banks and ditches of a Norman motte and bailey castle within its impressive prehistoric defensive earthworks: this site is a minor tourist attraction and has a dedicated car park (see photos on pages 64, 65 and 96).

Slapton Castle, like Halwell Camp, is an Iron Age hillfort (roughly between 750 BCE and 42 CE). But the fifth point of our star is a mystery. There are

many reasons that ancient monuments disappear from the landscape:
we have already noted that most of Bickleigh Brake's barrows have been
ploughed into oblivion, and barrows are not the only earthworks that have
been lost in this way. Standing stones and even stone circles can be cast
down and removed, and many ceremonial sites were made of wood that
has long since rotted and returned to the soil.

In the absence of evidence above ground, this problematical site is
identifiable only from the symmetry apparent in the rest of the star.
Unfortunately, the sheer size of some of the forts (Blackwell Rings, for
instance, encloses an oval area of around six acres (2.4 ha)) raises a
technical difficulty because ley lines often make merely glancing contact
with outer defences rather than neatly passing through the centre of the
site. How can we construct a reliable pattern from such imprecise markers?

Originally, of course, I become aware of the star pattern by accident
(the four markers don't exactly demand recognition). Then, in the absence
of a useful computer (I first noticed the star in the early 1980s), I used a
lengthy process of trial and error, and eventually narrowed down the search
until I discovered that the South Hams Star exhibits an extraordinary
geometric property: six of its key lines are the same length.

Using this geometry it is possible to be fairly accurate about the location
of the missing point, which may be reckoned to lie on the crest of a ridge
overlooking Kingsbridge: the A381 runs along this ridge and the site[11] is less
than three quarters of a mile (1.2km) from the town centre.

The only feature marked on the 1:25,000 Ordnance Survey map is a well,
but a visit to the site revealed this to be no ancient healing or holy well but
a modern contraption serving livestock. Mind you, there is a local tradition
that its position was determined by a water diviner or dowser.

To settle the matter of whether the star actually exists, we may need to wait
for non-destructive archaeological tools such as geophysical scans, which
can reveal whether this site is keeping a mighty secret, or whether the
whole idea is as imaginary as the lines between stars in the sky that define
the constellations.

---

[11] Grid reference SX 741450.

Prehistoric astronomical alignments

Stonehenge is probably the world's best known example of ancient astronomical architecture, but there are analogous sites all around the globe, ranging from the pyramids of Egypt to the pyramids of Central America, with sophisticated astronomical alignments. There are also plenty in Britain, and not only prehistoric structures but more recent ones as well — for more than a millennium, parish churches have maintained this tradition of sacred architecture by orienting the chancel towards the rising sun. And there have been suggestions that an analogous feat of prehistoric design took place at Capton.

When David Lloyd owned the vineyard at Capton he became fascinated by the hundreds of flint tools he found scattered over the hillside, and he developed his discovery into a tourist attraction in the early 1980s by building a replica of a prehistoric hut and opening a museum. He was also interested in archaeoastronomy and exhibited a map showing sighting lines, which radiated from his hilltop.[12] These lines connected with points on the horizon where the sun rose or set on important dates (such as the solstices, and also at the so-called 'cross-quarter days' such as May Day and Hallowe'en).

When he commissioned me to write a booklet about the archaeological history of the site[13] I devoted the final page to a consideration of possible alignments, and broadly endorsed David's findings that the Capton hilltop appeared to be the hub of a network of influence that spread throughout the South Hams, and which determined the location of various ancient sites. I used a mathematical formula (with about ten variables)[14] to reconstruct astronomical events within the timeframe of the many stone tools from Capton that were contemporary with Stonehenge.

Whereas Stonehenge is literally a masterpiece and the culmination of a culture's skill and knowledge writ in stone, I felt I would be dealing with a relatively crude rustic calendar — a mere seasonal sundial in comparison — and I did not anticipate pinpoint accuracy in the positions of whatever markers might have survived. Indeed, I assumed most markers would have been overgrown and lost, or overwhelmed and destroyed by farming. While this approach was not uncommon in those early days of the popular growth of the science of archaeoastronomy, and despite the fact that to the best of my knowledge the findings have never been challenged, I have taken the publication of this book as an opportunity to revisit them.

---

[12] Grid reference SX 83925362.

[13] Kenneth Taylor 1986, *Prehistoric Hill Settlement Capton*, Dartmouth, Prehistoric Hill Settlement Museum. My subsequent leaflet for the Museum bore the same name and was subtitled Archaeo Astronomy 2,000 B.C., and explored the suggested solar and lunar alignments in more detail.

[14] John Wood 1978, *Sun, Moon and Standing Stones,* Oxford, Oxford University Press.

*An eleven-circuit
medieval maze.*

*A seven-circuit Bronze
Age maze.*

Reassessing those proposed alignments in the light of present-day criteria for accuracy, the findings (such as a midwinter solstice line that apparently connected Oldstone Mansion, Blackawton church, and East Allington church) appear to lack rigour. Moreover, the cross-quarter days are a pastoral Celtic innovation that largely replaced the Neolithic calendar of astronomically significant days, and had no place in its originally agrarian / solar calendar. However tentative the remaining evidence, there still may be some wriggle-room for staunch supporters of the Capton alignment theory, and I should be delighted if somebody were to find proof of prehistoric design in the local landscape.

tHe patH of Life
— DANCING tHe maze

A high ridge rises to the south of Dartmouth Castle, lying parallel with the sea; its landward side slopes steeply into the valley that runs down into Warfleet, and on the very top of this ridge lies Gallions Boure (the spelling of its name has changed many times over the generations, and is now associated with the Civil War fort of Gallants Bower).

This windswept summit offers a fine panoramic view over the sea, and is now set among a patchwork of fields and is criss-crossed by hedges. The name Gallions Boure is first recorded on Thursday June 23rd, 1463, when Edward IV granted that the people of Dartmouth should keep a watch against enemies there. A document dated 1616 reports a lookout post at a site of this name, and further states that the usage was already regarded as an ancient tradition; their use of a compass to accurately measure the direction of the wind led to this area sometimes being called Compass Hill, a name also commemorated at Compass Cove.

The name Gallions Boure seems to have become corrupted several hundred years ago so that it now identifies the nearby Civil War fort lying about 660 yards (600m) along its northeast slope: Gallant's Bower. In fact, the name Gallant's Bower and its older variants are not unique to Dartmouth, or even to Devon. Despite research into the name's meaning, it remains uncertain but one intriguing interpretation suggests an important pagan site, a large, turf-cut, spiral dancing-maze.

Percy Russell[15] notes at least five Gallant's Bowers on the hilltops of Devon, and draws a parallel with the Julian's and Gillian's Bowers of the eastern counties of England. The illustrations show the structure of Julian's Bower, a medieval turf maze some 40 yards (37m) in circumference at Alkborough, Lincolnshire,[16] where May Eve games were enjoyed; and the Bronze Age version that is at least 3,500 years old.

William Shakespeare's play *A Midsummer Night's Dream* was first performed c.1595, and features Oberon, the King of the Fairies and his Queen, Titania. Although love triumphs in the end, temporary discord between this magical couple brought all manner of upset to the natural world; Titania laments the dire effects of their estrangement with a catalogue of woes such as famine and disease, and includes the observation that

> *"... the quaint mazes in the wanton green,*
> *For lack of tread, are undistinguishable"[17]*

There is, likewise, nothing to see at Gallions Boure today, and ramblers should almost certainly discount the humped remains of what is probably a 'pillow mound' or rabbit warren that predates the hedge system on the hill (it appears to have been completely ploughed away on the southern side of a hedge).[18]

Such mazes would, however, have been the focus for joyous fertility rites as well as solemn initiations into religious mysteries. Some folklorists affirm its symbolism can still be traced in certain folk customs and circle dances. Perhaps the perpetual round of festivities based on the farmers' calendar ensured its survival as a living institution for millennia. There may even have been a link, perhaps even a processional way, with the holy spring associated with the nearby site of the church of St Petrox.

Such a Bronze Age cult could have come to these shores with the Mediterranean traders whose relics associated with tin mining on Dartmoor (tin is an essential component of bronze). And, of course, the famous Brutus Stone at Totnes commemorates the legend of Bronze Age arrivals from the Mediterranean, famously told by Geoffrey of Monmouth, and which we shall examine in more depth presently. There is also a Bronze Age tumulus or burial mound at Brownstone, Kingswear, just across the river from Gallions Boure, and prehistoric flint tools have been found on the Gallions Boure hilltop itself.[19]

---

[15] Percy Russell 1950, *Dartmouth*, London, B T Batsford.

[16] This identical design is also the earliest (c.1390) surviving architectural example known in an English church — a gilded roof boss eight inches (0.2m) in diameter, in the north nave of St Mary Redcliffe church, Bristol.

[17] Act II, Scene I.

[18] Grid reference SX 88054975.

[19] I was fortunate enough to acquire a particularly fine specimen that I donated to Dartmouth Museum, where it is still displayed.

A sacred maze would have been an important focus of religious ritual in the Bronze Age and, given the perennial popularity of springtime and early summer festivities with young people (of all ages), the site could conceivably have remained in use until such celebrations were suppressed by Christian elders. The widespread adoption of the maze into medieval church architecture, though, amply demonstrates the enduring appeal of the design. There is something oddly fulfilling about finding your way into the centre, and then tracing your path out again — even if you disregard any notion of sacred symbolism.

Buddhists, and others who pay attention to the machinations of the human mind, will appreciate the analogy between a maze and any captivating idea or project. As soon as we enter we usually have little option but to run the course, working through the chain of events from beginning to end, and then heave a sigh of relief and (hopefully) satisfaction when we return to freedom — back where we began. Hopefully too we shall be a little the wiser for having made the journey. Certainly many generations of Christians who thread their way through the holy maze perceive the act as a spiritual pilgrimage, and find the whole process cathartic. But, as the myth of Theseus and the Minotaur relates, sometimes what awaits us at the centre of the maze can be as perilous and challenging as facing up to fear itself.

SYNCHRONICITY

Coincidences can have consequences that shape our lives, especially when they resonate with something in our subconscious: for example giving us an idea to visit a special place or person. Coincidences that achieve this can be said to have a special meaning for us, and Carl Jung coined the word 'synchronicity' to describe them. Some powerful synchronistic experiences can be life-changing, and may even be interpreted in a spiritual light as a personal message — announcing the immanence of the divine. There have been so many peculiar coincidences during the writing of this book that I could almost fill a fifth chapter with examples, but a representative sample will suffice to give the flavour of this common yet fascinating experience.

The first tale concerns how I came to write this book, and begins when I set up a small publishing business the year before I left Dartmouth in the mid 1980s. Its very first publication was a slim pamphlet entitled *Paranormal Dertemouthe*,[20] which contained accounts of some ghostly phenomena in the town (it has been a pleasure to update them for inclusion in this volume). Naturally, at that time I was at the very start of a steep learning curve and, although not below average for the genre at that time, frankly the book wasn't very well produced. I always planned to print a revised edition but when I moved away I never quite got around to that 2nd edition.

---

[20] Ken Taylor 1985, *Paranormal Dertemouthe*, Dartmouth, Carmina Publishing.

'Dertemouthe' is how Dartmouth was spelled in Chaucer's *The Canterbury Tales*, and I used the old-fashioned version as a reference to the rich history of the town and the many traditional tales that have their roots in centuries past. What I didn't know until I started researching the current volume in 2004, was that the General Prologue to the Tales mentions Dertemouthe in relation to a 'Shipman' or seafarer, whose ship was the Maudelayne (Madeleine). The coincidence is that I first arrived in Dartmouth completely by chance when I was invited to join a friend living on a converted fishing vessel moored near the Hermitage Castle in Old Mill Creek — the *MV Madeleine*. What are the odds against that?

A more common example, and one that happens to a lot people, is when you start thinking of someone, and you unexpectedly hear from them. That happened to a contributor I hadn't been in touch with for months: I had written to the family hoping to clarify a minor point of a story, and promptly received the reply along with the following anecdote.

"Strange thing happened today to my Mum, when I rang her and started to tell her about your email, she said 'Hold on. That's odd. I was on the bus today going home, and it suddenly occurred to me that I had not heard any more about the book, and had resolved to go in to The Harbour Bookshop next time I went into town and ask about it, all I was waiting to do was to ask you the name of the chap who was writing it, because I could only remember he was called Ken!' How strange was that!?"

Perhaps though, that may be an example of telepathy rather than coincidence or synchronicity.

Following my stay in the haunted room at the Royal Castle Hotel, I interviewed its owner Nigel Way, and we touched upon the publicity value of having a ghost story attached to the premises. He broadly shrugged it off while admitting that they did occasionally have an enquiry about the ghosts. I was happy to say that earlier that very morning I had been at the reception desk when a phone call came through and the caller requested a room with a ghost. The request was rare enough to visibly startle the receptionist (although she was professional enough to not give her caller any embarrassment), but she would have been less surprised had it not been for my visit, as the hotel staff had been buzzing with talk about ghosts all morning.

Finally, close to the completion of the manuscript I had an idea for a future book devoted to trees, so I surfed the Web and joined a promising new e-group that covered all aspects — from forestry to folklore.[21] I wrote an introductory piece about Yggdrasil — the Teutonic ash tree of life — and, as a throwaway remark, tacked on a note that I had vaguely heard of an ash tree charm.

---

[21] http://groups.yahoo.com/group/treetribe .

To my surprise I received a reply from a member of the group, Lexie Devine, who said that passing ill children through a split trunk used to be a fairly common practice, and she had "just been reading about it." This prompted me to re-find, research and write the story of the Kingswear ash charm (see preceding chapter), and although she was the only who seemed to be interested, I sent a copy of the story to the e-group.

Lexie replied saying the ash charm "is on my list to investigate further as part of my Druidic studies.[22] As an interesting curiosity, the little babe you mention... shares my birthday. Curious coincidence, huh!" And she added "I have long been a believer in coincidence being so much more than simply something to comment on, then ignore. I seem to find that when I am on a path and need guidance, just the right book or person will pop up and help me on my way. I always take notice of coincidences as they usually have a message for me."

What makes this particularly memorable for me is that our correspondence occurred at the very time I was compiling this section on synchronicity.

the devil's fire

The human mind is easily fooled into thinking that the very unusual is actually unnatural, as is demonstrated by this apparent case of spontaneous human combustion that occurred in Lower Street and was reported by the Devonshire Association.[23] The victim, identified only as Madam H, was a keen card player and although her 'quaint old house' was a popular social venue on a Saturday evening, her passion for gaming regularly defeated the stamina of her opponents. It was customary therefore, for her to sit alone in the parlour until well past midnight, pitting her wits against a 'dummy' hand.

One Sunday morning her bed was discovered not to have been slept in, and when the house was searched a pile of cremated bone and cinders was found beside her card table. Superstitious folk reckoned she had finally met her match at gambling, and swore that it was no ordinary dummy playing against her that night. Her opponent, they maintained, had been the Devil himself and he had won her at last, body and soul.

things that go whooo in the night

"A few years ago," Howard Garner told me in 2005, "at the bar, a guest said he had a very vivid dream: he was by the rocks by the sea in the cove, and there was a railway just above, with a steam train going along."

---

[22] She is Grove Chief of the Hawk's Oak Grove (http://groups.yahoo.com/group/Hawks_Oak_Grove).
[23] 1879, Collectanea Curiosa Devoniensia, *Transactions of the Devonshire Association*, 11, 346.

The bar in question is at Greyhomes, a small country house offering luxury art deco apartments with panoramic views over Slapton Ley, and there isn't a railway for miles. However, a couple overheard this comment, and Howard was struck by the look of surprise on their faces.

"Isn't that strange?" said the woman, and gestured to her husband. "He said he woke up in the middle of the night when he heard a train whistle."

Howard couldn't help but wonder whether there was "a sound that seeped into their subconscious" that caused them both to think of trains. Our sense of hearing is a vital survival mechanism, and it doesn't completely turn off when we sleep (which is why alarm clocks manage to wake us up, mostly), so his rational explanation has a lot of merit. In fact, weird dreams are easily stimulated by natural noises in the night — the seagulls that rove like a mad hunt through the sky in the pre-dawn hours may inspire all manner of frightful episodes, especially in the dreams of visitors from inland areas. But what on earth could suggest a steam train?

things that go *bang* in the day

Stephen Baker told me a rather odd story about his home in Slapton — Rock Cottage. It happened in May or June 2002 when he was renovating the interior of the building and "hacking plaster off the walls." This work made a lot of noise and went on steadily day after day for at least a week, and was particularly loud because the house was gutted and each stroke echoed off the bare masonry. The Queen's Arms pub is a stone's throw away and is Stephen's local, so when he popped in one evening the conversation naturally turned to how his building was getting on. His companion, who heard the din on a daily basis, happened to comment that the banging had started particularly early that morning, around 7am, and had continued throughout the day. But the weird thing was that Stephen had spent the whole day at Torcross reading a friend's university dissertation, and had only just returned to Slapton around 7pm when he went to the bar. The house had been empty all day. Sadly, unlike in fairytales of industrious and helpful elves, Stephen didn't find his work had all been done for him.

vampire with cloven hooves?

A small house at Penlee, near the cliffs of Matthew's Point, Strete, was the scene of a bizarre event that author and occultist Montague Summers claimed to have been caused by a vampire.[24] Mrs Hughes had taken up residence in June 1918, and she was

[24] Montague Summers 1929, *The Vampire in Europe*, London, Kegan, Paul, Trench, Trubner & Co Ltd, xi.

the sole occupier apart from a friend who was visiting. One morning they came down stairs and were astonished upon entering the sitting room, to find a muddy footprint in the middle of the polished parquet floor. Their upset took on a sinister dimension when closer inspection revealed the print was clearly that of a cloven hoof.

Despite realising that it was impossible for a large animal to have entered the house (the windows were far too small), they searched the property carefully for any signs of further disturbance — but there were none.

Summers remarks on the traditional association between cloven hooves and the Devil, and mentioned that his footprints had been left elsewhere in Devon, most notably in the snow on the night of Thursday February 8th, 1855, where the tracks were traced all the way from Exmouth to Totnes. However, what happened next at Penlee convinced him that Mrs Hughes was not the victim of a satanic manifestation, but of a vampire's incipient attack.

Over the next few nights Mrs Hughes was subjected to physical assaults from an invisible being that left her badly frightened. In the end she resorted to hanging garlic all over her home, which, she said, worked like a charm, and peace was finally restored. It was the success of this traditional remedy against vampires that left Summers in no doubt that the disturbances had been caused by a vampire.

He further speculated that this vampire was perhaps old or somehow weakened, and that it was unable to mount the bloodthirsty attack normally associated with creatures of its kind. Summers conjures a vivid picture of what might have happened had Mrs Hughes not found the way to cleanse her home of her malign and uninvited guest, allowing the vampire to grow stronger until it was able to capture her in its inhuman embrace.

cLoveN hooves, aND StoNe circLes

In or around February 1994 Stevie Rogers was confronted by a shocking sight that aroused her instinct to get away — quickly — from something so blatant in its defiance of common sense that it conjured a sense of imminent otherworldly danger.

She was alone in the snow-mantled countryside of Fast Rabbit Farm near Ash, and the sense of isolation was as profound as the silence. The snow was drifting in places, and her journey to check on and deliver hay to her sheep had taken thirty minutes instead of the usual seven or eight because she had to dig her way through the drifts. Her mid-morning journey was part and parcel of the arduous life expected by anyone who loves their livestock, but what she found in the field was not part of the natural order of things.

There are no lanes in that part of the farm, and she was driving around the edge of an empty 20 acre (8.1 ha) field immediately before the field with the sheep when she noticed a trail of footprints in the snow. The tracks had been left by a creature with cloven hooves about the size of the palm of her hand, which had approached the gate. A glance at the undisturbed snow showed that the tracks didn't go past the gate — the beast should still have been standing right there in front of her.

When she looked to see where it had come from she saw that the spacing was like that of a pacing man rather than a four-legged animal and, rather than meandering, it walked a dead straight path. She followed the tracks back out towards the middle of the field, about a hundred feet or so (30m), where they began — as abruptly as they'd stopped at the gate. Surrounded by pristine snow all around, the first cloven hoof print simply appeared out of nowhere.

She returned the following day but a further fall of snow during the night had covered all traces. However, a second mysterious event occurred in another field the following November on a very foggy day where she couldn't see clearly beyond about ten feet (3m). Again, she was attending to her flock there, when she literally stumbled over some stones, which was odd because the field was a pasture simply covered with grass.

The stones were bigger than pebbles but small enough to hold in one hand, and had been laid in a perfect circle, with none of them touching the next. She chanced upon half-a-dozen of these circles, which were about 5 feet (1.5m) across, and noted that they were all perfect, despite the sheep milling around, none of the stones had been displaced.

Stevie returned later in the day but all the stones had been removed. She kindly reconstructed a circle for me, and found it was not easy to source stones even for the one example, which contained eighteen stones. These bizarre events so impressed her that she invited author and healer Natasha Hoffman and her partner and co-author Hamilton Hill to visit and offer their insights. They walked the fields together and Natasha used a pendulum with a bob that looked like amber, to dowse the site of a Bronze Age settlement that had been revealed earlier by aerial photography. Natasha and Hamilton claimed the once thriving community had been torn apart by a family feud that had turned deadly, and that although the murderer had fled, the settlement — now tainted and rendered unwholesome by the bloodshed — was abandoned by all save his aged parents who were left behind, shunned and alone. Their spirits, Natasha claimed, were still there — lost, confused, and trapped.

Whether such traumatic events could have had anything to do with the paranormal visitations in the locality is open to debate, but Natasha and Hamilton offered the spirits the assistance they seemed to need, and enabled them to move on after perhaps three thousand years of haunting the site; and nothing odd has been reported since. Stevie, who runs a landscaping business, bought the farm in 1987, and created an exquisite woodland garden featuring an excavated lake fed by natural springs, not far from the fields. This garden is occasionally open to the public — details are on her website.[25]

---

[25] http://www.fastrabbitfarm.co.uk .

when giants roamed this land

The story of how Brutus sailed into the mouth of the Dart and, accompanied by a fleet laden with treasure, reached landfall at Totnes is well known locally; and is recounted at length by Geoffrey of Monmouth.[26] Brutus was leader of a band known as Trojans because they were descendents (mostly third or fourth generation) of the survivors of the fallen city of Troy (c.1230 — 1180 BCE,), whose overthrow was made famous by the poet Homer in the *Iliad* around 800 BCE.

Brutus had wandered the Mediterranean for many years, gathering these displaced but still proud people into a formidable army, when they chanced upon a temple of the virginal huntress and moon goddess Diana on a deserted island. In the company of thirteen men, Brutus ceremoniously donned a headband, and approached her statue in the temple. They set up altars to Jupiter, Mercury and to Diana herself in front of her statue, and poured libations to each in turn. Then Brutus held aloft in his right hand the sacred vessel containing a mixture of wine and the blood of pure white hind; and he broke the silence by addressing the goddess. Calling to mind and praising her powers, he asked her to reveal the place where he could finally settle and, amid the singing of maidens, dedicate temples to her.

He made this conjuration nine times, walked around her altar four times, and lay down on the skin of the hind that had been stretched there on the ground. At length, he fell asleep and, around the third hour after sunset, he awoke and proclaimed that Diana had appeared to him and given him directions to an island beyond the sunset that had been populated by giants. There, she said, he would found a dynasty whose dominion would encircle the earth.

Although Brutus professed to some doubt whether this was a true vision of the goddess, or merely a dream, his advisors were happy to accept it at face value. They returned to their companions at the ships, and set sail in a wind that bore them steadily west.

Further adventures beset them before they reached the shores of Albion at Totnes where they founded their nation. Millennia later, in the Victorian era, it seemed to fulfil its prophesied destiny when its leaders were able to boast the sun never set on the British Empire — e.g. it truly circled the globe. Before this kingdom could be established however, there was one small matter to sort out: instead of being empty of giants as Diana had promised, there were still some wandering about. So the Britons (so called now, in honour of Brutus) attacked them and left them scattered and hiding in out-of-the-way hillside or mountain caves.

Goemagot, a giant who stood twelve feet (3.7m) tall and could uproot an oak tree with his bare hands, launched a counter attack or reprisal raid with twenty of his fellows. Brutus and his men were caught off guard while they were at Totnes

---

[26] Geoffrey of Monmouth c.1136, *The History of the Kings of Britain*

celebrating a holy festival, and many Britons were slaughtered before they rallied and defeated the giants, all of whom were slain except, at the command of Brutus, Goemagot himself. Not that Brutus was being merciful when he ordered Goemagot to be spared, far from it: the giant was kept alive to provide sport — he faced a fight to the death with the Briton's best unarmed combat expert, Corineus.

Although Corineus was wounded in the duel, he managed to lift Goemagot off the ground and run with him to the coast nearby, where he tossed him from a cliff into the sea — the giant's body was sundered by sharp rocks, and the water turned red with his blood.

Now although this is a wonderful local story, and the image of the Trojan fleet sailing past Dartmouth is one to savour, I should not have included it in this volume were it not for the fact that Kingswear has a claim to be the site of Goemagot's death and, as it were, burial at sea.

The strangely-named medieval tower house Gommerock, whose ruin sits above the rocky coast at Kingswear, was recorded in 1580 as being called Godmerock, which some researchers think may derive from a Scandinavian or Old English personal name such as Godmer or Godmaer (the antiquity of either source argues that the name had belonged to the land for centuries before the house was built). A number of folklorists however,[27] have noted the similarity of the name to the equally odd-sounding Goemagot, which has numerous variants of pronunciation and spelling including Goemagog and Gogmagog.

It is hard to say whether the place-name derives from the legendary giant, or whether Geoffrey of Monmouth took the place-name and gave it to his giant (a theory favoured by John Clark[28]), or even whether there is any connection beyond the theorising of folklorists. There are certainly some other contenders for the distinction of being the site of Goemagot's doom: Plymouth Hoe had a turf-cut figure (or figures) already called Gogmagog by 1486 and has a long-standing traditional claim; Theo Brown suggested Stoke Fleming as a possible site because the red stone of its cliffs stains the tide a ruddy hue; and Totnes folklorist Bob Mann told me he considers Berry Head to be the most likely spot.

Personally, I favour stories that have a tidy plot, so rounding off the story of the Trojan Conquest with the bones of the last native giant of Albion lodging among the rocky teeth that line the mouth of the Dart — the point at which the invaders had first arrived — makes good mythological sense to me. Like the spirit of a sacrificial victim,

---

[27] Including Theo Brown 1955, The Trojans in Devon, *Transactions of the Devonshire Association*, 87.

[28] John Clark extensively explored and championed the Goemagot — Gommerock connection in 2002, in his article Gogmagog Again, in *3rd Stone*, issue 44.

Goemagot lingers here as a guardian, ever vigilant against the country's enemies. (As previously noted, in Chapter 2, one of the ghosts of Gommerock performs an identical duty albeit at a more personal level.)

Gommerock was once a stout medieval fortified house, a five-sided structure with walls up to five feet (1.8m) thick. It is likely to be at least 14th century in date as it appears to be the subject of a licence granted in 1402 during the turbulent reign of Henry IV, allowing it to be modified for improved defence. From the 1480s it guarded the eastern terminus of a great chain that reached across the river to Dartmouth Castle, and which could be pulled taut to prevent enemy ships entering the Dart. Its key role as a military institution waned from 1501 when Kingswear castle was constructed.

Even if the place-name Gommerock might once have applied to a larger area, perhaps even to the whole headland with its reef of Shooter Rock, Shag Stone and Mew Stone, and the Eastern Black Rock, the naming of Godmerock Castelle was perfectly in keeping with my view of the defensive function of Goemagot's emplacement at this strategic point.

sea serpent

There was a spate of sightings of a giant sea serpent around the south coast in the 1930s, and one of the most celebrated incidents occurred at Redlap Cove, Stoke Fleming, where Harold Groves had a close encounter with the beastie in the autumn of 1937.[29]

He first saw it out to sea beyond the cove, heading towards Dartmouth. It was arching its body clear out of the water as it swam, but otherwise looked like a giant conger eel — until, that is, it came to within six feet (1.8m) of where he stood on the high tide line. It reared up in front of him, reaching a couple of feet (0.6m) out of the water, and its head looked like a cross between a camel and a sheep, but was pallid and hairless except for a small clump of hair or bristles on the top.

The two observed each other closely, and Mr Groves noted that the creature's eyes protruded somewhat from the sides of its head. Whilst we cannot begin to fathom what the creature thought of Mr Groves, it did not attack him but simply withdrew beneath the waves.

Perhaps it was a descendent of this beastie that gave a local ferryman a soaking. Kevin Pyne told me that in the 1970s he worked on the lower car ferry with a colleague from Kingswear, and after the shift Kevin used to drop him off and row home to Dartmouth. Kevin recalls rowing back on one occasion very clearly — it was about 11pm and "at the top of the tide. Nice and calm, beautiful stars out, just minding my own business rowing across the river, and whoosh! Splash. And up

[29] Ronnie Hoyle 1993, *Strange Tales of the South West*, Bodmin, Bossiney Books.

I went and — boom — down. Soaked I was… Whatever it was (don't forget you're not looking where you're going when you're rowing a boat) came up and there was an almighty sort of splash and, well, I was wet."

He added "When I mentioned it to the other ferrymen, now sadly all dead, they just said 'Ah it happened to you as well then did it?' I never rowed across the Dart so fast in my life, and for months after."

To a cryptozoologist familiar with sightings of weird creatures from all over the world, this Dartmouth monster it is simply a rare sighting of an animal as yet unknown to science but, because it is not yet accepted into the compass of normal, everyday life, it still deserves a place here amongst the paranormal. Although a dragon would not only warrant inclusion but would be a star attraction in this menagerie of the strange, the only ones I've found are a bit disappointing. The 'dragon beams' in the ceiling of the ground floor bar at The Cherub, Dartmouth, are not the long bones of a local dragon defeated by some maiden-saving knight, but simply an architectural term for the wooden beams positioned diagonally, rather than parallel with the walls. And the other famous dragon in the area, the Green Dragon public house, Church Street, Stoke Fleming, is unsure where its name came from (and although its website mentions a ghost on the premises, I was equally unable to confirm the details).[30]

a Lost masonic treasure?

There is an intriguing mystery at the Britannia Royal Naval College (BRNC) regarding the laying of a commemorative stone on Friday March 7th, 1902, by King Edward VII.[31] Contemporary accounts offer contradictory descriptions of the time capsule that was deposited during the ceremony: *The Sphere* offers us a stout chest made from the oak timbers of HMS *Britannia*, with copper fittings; while the *Dartmouth Chronicle* regaled its readers with a richly enamelled casket of solid silver covered in gold, embellished with medallions of Dartmouth Castle and Kingswear Castle. It seems incredible that either journalist could make such a mistake in their coverage of this prestigious royal event, so we are left wondering — were there two boxes?

The mystery seemed about to be solved in 2005 when the college dismantled the masonry around the inscription celebrating King Edward's visit, and found a cavity beneath the stone. There lay the wooden chest encased in its art nouveau metalwork, along with the purple ribbon with pure gold tassels that had been used to lower it into its granite sepulchre. When the wooden lid with the royal monogram was lifted, the chest was found to contain five newspapers and a set of coins that,

---

[30] Peter & Alix Crowther, *History*, http://www.green-dragon-pub.co.uk/history.htm .
[31] Dr Jane Harrold and Dr Richard Porter 2005, *Britannia Royal Naval College 1905 - 2005*, Dartmouth, Richard Webb.

along with the carefully conserved chest, are on display in the college museum. But the gilt casket had not been found — could there be another cavity elsewhere?

Speculation soon fixed on the fact that Edward VII had been Grand Master of the Freemasons for twenty-five years until his accession to the throne in 1901 when he became Protector of the Craft. He had conducted many Masonic ceremonies in public at the laying of foundations for public buildings, bridges, and churches (including the cathedral at Truro), and there is every likelihood that the BRNC had been given the royal Masonic seal of approval — does Masonic ritual offer us any clues?

Masonic cornerstone ceremonies often include deposits such as time capsules that seem to answer a primal human instinct for ritual sacrifice at the commencement of monumental works. The preferred location of these cornerstones has always been the northeast corner of a building, a position significant in Masonic lore because it marks the mid point between the dark of night (north) and the dawning light (east), which is indeed apt for a building rearing up out of its shady foundations and into the full light of day. Might there have been a second, secret ceremony?

Identification of a candidate cornerstone in the northeast of the college, which would have been the chapel, is made easier because Masonic tradition suggests that such a stone should have measured sixteen inches square (40.6 x 40.6cm). But all attempts at locating this second stone have so far failed, and the mystery remains. So, until this second precious relic is found and opened (the Protector of the Craft locked it with a special golden key), we can only speculate about its contents, which were reported to consist of a manuscript, just a loyal address from local dignitaries, in support of their king.

king arthur

There is a rumour that King Arthur's magic sword Excalibur lies in Slapton Ley, and that he himself sailed away to the mystic Isle of Avalon from Slapton Sands. This idea, promoted by Marion Smithes,[32] seems based on the following verse in the last 'book' of the epic poem *Idylls of the King*, by Alfred, Lord Tennyson, which describes what happened after Arthur fell in the final battle.

> *... because his wound was deep,*
> *The bold Sir Bedivere uplifted him,*
> *And bore him to a chapel nigh the field,*
> *A broken chancel with a broken cross,*
> *That stood on a dark strait of barren land:*
> *On one side lay the Ocean, and on one*
> *Lay a great water, and the moon was full.*

---

[32] Marion F. Smithies 1933, *Strete Past and Present*, Dartmouth, R Cranford & Son.

Tennyson identifies the location as Lyonesse, a mysterious region located somewhere toward the western extremity of England that is usually associated with Land's End (and beyond), but anyone familiar with Slapton's unusual lagoon beside the sea could be tempted to claim it as this key site of Arthurian legend. The chapel cannot be recognised from this description, but there are mentions of cliffs in the poem, that with a little willing suspension of disbelief perhaps, could indicate it may once have stood above the bluffs at Torcross.

The king was too badly wounded to stand, and so asked Sir Bedivere to cast Excalibur into the middle of the mere. Upon his return, Sir Bedivere told Arthur how he shut his eyes as he threw away the sword (referred to as 'him'), but finally looked to see how Excalibur was received into the safekeeping of the Lady of the Lake.

> *... with both hands I flung him, wheeling him;*
> *But when I looked again, behold an arm,*
> *Clothed in white samite, mystic, wonderful,*
> *That caught him by the hilt, and brandished him*
> *Three times, and drew him under in the mere.*

Of course it would be folly to confuse myth with historical fact, and it would be doubly foolish to contend that this location is the only possible site of Arthur's last battle. Arthurian legend belongs to the whole nation, ennobling people everywhere. One thing seems certain though: Avalon is to be found in the fond and evergreen hopes of the human heart, where the spirit of Arthur resides — restored to full vigour and eternally vigilant — chivalrous champion of our perpetual right to freedom.

index

All named places are in Dartmouth
unless indicated otherwise.

Page numbers in *italic* indicate an illustration.

Adrian Good

ken taylor – the author

Ken Taylor arrived in Dartmouth as a young man in 1981. He had been raised in Ideford, Devon, in a house reputed to have two ghosts, but never understood why they were there — his parents built the house on a green field site. It may, he thought, be significant that the field had been a traditional camping ground for Romany travellers.

Perhaps some of the gipsy influence rubbed off on him as he didn't settle into a routine career path; instead a bohemian lifestyle allowed him a broad range of experience, including jobs as diverse as an insurance clerk in Exeter, a foundry worker in Amsterdam, an archaeologist in Chester, and a gravedigger in the Shetland Isles. In Dartmouth, though, he found his vocation as a writer, contributing poems to *The Dartmouth Chronicle* and articles to various local magazines.

By the time he left the town in 1985 he also had a number of short stories to his credit, and was proprietor of a small publishing business that kept him busy for seven years. Thereafter he devoted his time to writing and, following publication of some three hundred freelance articles, he started writing full-length books with Mind-Body-Spirit themes: four have appeared in his own name, plus a further five in collaboration with his wife Joules. A comprehensive booklist can be found at www.wavewrights.com .

Despite living most of his life in Devon, Ken currently lives in Bristol, and the family home includes their son, a dog, three cats, a tarantula, a large urban garden full of wildlife, and yes — perhaps even a ghost.

valerie wills – the photographer

Valerie Wills is married with two sons and lives in Dartmouth where her family connections go back many years.

She studied photography at Loughton College, Essex covering all aspects of conventional photography and specialising in printing techniques and design.

With the advent of digital photography Valerie was fascinated by the possibilities of this new technology. In particular the Photoshop computer programme has added a new dimension to her photography and to the enhancement of her digital images.

For the majority of the photos taken for this book she used Nikon D100 and Nikkor ED 17-35 lens.

Valerie also works with Nikon F4 and F801 conventional film cameras with a variety of Nikon lenses digitalised through Nikon Cool Scan and Adobe Photoshop CS.

Her previous commissions have included photography for Robert Hale Publishers, the Rolex Watch Company and the Guide Dogs for the Blind Association.

Her work from *Dartmouth Ghosts & Mysteries* was exhibited at The Flavel, Dartmouth to coincide with its publication.